WELCOME TO TOMBSTONE

WELCOME
TO TOMBSTONE

By

JAN OLOF OLSSON

Translated from the Swedish by

MAURICE MICHAEL

LONDON

ELEK BOOKS

This translation copyright 1956 by Elek Books Limited

Published by
ELEK BOOKS LIMITED
14 Great James Street
London, W.C.1
and simultaneously in Canada by the
Ryerson Press
299 Queen Street West
Toronto 2b
Canada

Printed in Great Britain by
Page Bros. (Norwich) Limited, Norwich

CONTENTS

ILLUSTRATIONS

THE WAY WEST

I HAD been a long time in America before it occurred to me that I might go out West. Perhaps it was Jansson and his thumb which started me; in fact, queerly enough, I believe it must have been. Jansson had come sweeping into the Greek Bar on Atlantic Avenue one stormy night. He had a kitbag on his shoulder and his right hand in bandages. He immediately spotted us as Swedes and spoke to us in a suave manner I found surprising until I later discovered that he had once been a waiter in Gothenburg.

"Jansson. Yes, thanks. Just in from Puerto Rico. Pleasant job in a hotel. Luxury hotel. What donnas! But there was always shooting on the street at night when you went home, and I'm a bit fat these days, getting that way at least, and can't bend double like I could in my glory. And then my papers weren't quite in order either. And that's the devil. I haven't had my papers in order for I don't know how long. I had to pack and get out. Took a foul job on a Norwegian just to get away, signed on as pantry-boy though I'm nearly forty. Then one day I went on my head in the potato-cellar when I went below and the bloody boat was rolling, and got a nail in my thumb. The mate treated my thumb, but whatever he did, it just got bigger and bigger. In the end he had to give me an injection of pain-killer, and he put it right into a muscle in my leg. Darned funny, I can tell you."

Jansson had ordered a whisky; when he got it he raised his glass to us and tossed it off in one gulp. We inspected his thumb which really was worth looking at. It was enveloped in bandage and right at the end, far too small for the bandage, sat a finger-stall which, far from covering it, was just like a tiny cap on an immense head.

Jansson moved into the Norwegian Seamen's Home and got a room in the same corridor as mine. We often visited each other and drank a little pocket-flask of Philadelphia whisky which was enough for about two glasses each and cost ninety-five cents. He had an amusing way of telling the most astounding stories, how

7

he had been torpedoed on convoy duty, been chucker-out at a pornographic cabaret in Havana and lived for a time in Peru.

"It was there I got so fat," he confessed. "I had two girls, one in the town with a pleasant little flat and one in a village out in the country, and they both just stuffed food into me. It's not true that you can get your weight down after that. Of course there was trouble. One evening we quarrelled and I slipped in the alcove and knocked in a cupboard door. Look."

Jansson showed me a great scar above one ear. I wondered to myself what that girl in Peru had hit him with.

Even when telling his stories in the centre of Brooklyn he remained typically Swedish and typically a waiter. He used to tell me about a little cabin he had helped his parents buy out of his convoy and risk-money. He had set out photographs, one of his parents and a sister in a student's cap and another of a brother sitting at the wheel of a 1939 car in the main street of a Lapland hamlet. Sometimes of an evening and almost every Sunday he would drag me to the Scandinavian Seamen's Church beyond Court Street, and there we transformed the entire building into a Swedish church hall with a lot of embarrassed people. He was passionately fond of playing ping-pong, which always disturbed a number of old mates who just wanted to sit quietly reading the local papers from their home towns in Sweden and Norway, and then we drank coffee. He knew the girl who acted as waitress in the church hall and though she was an out-and-out New Yorker he could manage to make her giggle like any country hoyden.

Jansson had not been home for ten years. In his childhood he had been at the old naval boys' school in Karlskrona.

"I wouldn't wish my worst enemy there," he said. He had run away from it because he was thrashed too often and somehow Sweden and that school had been linked in his mind as his idea of hell. The last time he had been home, after many years as ordinary seaman and steward, he had driven into Karlskrona and gone to the old parade ground where he had marched up and down as a boy, but after his spell as a waiter he had wasted no time in getting back to sea and the ports and high wages. He never wrote home, though he began many letters, even while we lived in the same corridor, but he always gave up after a day or two, and having his thumb to blame made him feel better.

8

"I never have anything to say."

But one day he went to the consulate and arranged to have money sent home.

He was always to some extent the gracious, slightly ingratiating waiter. One evening we were in his room drinking a little Philadelphia when, in the middle of a sentence of some tale about Havana he was telling, he vomited. He managed it with real presence of mind and elegance, just drew the waste-paper basket towards him with his foot and deposited it there, and then went on talking as though nothing had happened.

A little while later, seeing me still looking surprised, he explained: "I'm sitting almost on the radiator and that always makes you sick in the end."

It was Jansson's thumb which had brought him to New York. He was trying to get the shipping company to pay him compensation for loss of earnings and pain endured. Every morning he would set out to the consulate to discuss his thumb with the company and a lawyer. He came back during the afternoon and then had dinner, pork sausage or cod, at the Norwegian restaurant. He wielded knife and fork with such elegance that you never thought of his thumb.

One evening when I went into the Greek Bar round the corner I saw Jansson sitting with a couple of fat men in well-pressed suits and with black greasy hair. It was a common type in that part of Brooklyn round Atlantic Avenue. In the Seamen's Home we called them gorillas or torpedoes, and we had a vague idea that they were crooks and gangsters but didn't rightly know what they did. Jansson was immersed in quiet earnest conversation with the two torpedoes, and when he caught sight of me in the distance he shook his head slightly and gave me a wink, so that I should know to keep away. I seated myself at the counter to have a lettuce sandwich and a beer and gazed at a picture which some Swedish or Norwegian sailor must have left behind as payment. It was of a ship on the crest of a high wave and with a town in the background such as could only exist in the homesick mind of a Scandinavian sailor, with girls in white dresses and a large white wooden hotel on the beach.

I had just finished, when Jansson came up and asked how many dollars I had on me or could get hold of quickly.

"Thirty-five, forty," said I. "But I have to pay for my room

9

on Friday. Fifteen seventy-five. That will leave me with twenty dollars."

"No more?"

"No. Well, that's to say I hope to get money in a few days, but I don't know when. Twenty dollars. And I've got to eat."

"You see, I've got an address and a tip from those torpedoes. You know the old Russian who sells chocolate and cigarettes somewhere round the corner. He's a bookmaker. I've got a sure horse from the torpedoes and they said I could put money on with that old chap. Money for jam, they said."

I gave Jansson a long and reproachful look; he had lived in Puerto Rico and Peru and was full of worldly wisdom and well versed in the way to deal with crooks and in the art of living on the shady side of life, and yet he had fallen for that simple con-man's trick. And I told him so.

But Jansson was of a different opinion. It was shady of course, he said; in fact, it was probably a good deal shadier than he or I realised. It was crooked in a very complicated way, for those torpedoes would not have taken the trouble to sit there trying to persuade a chance seaman to put his last few dollars on with a Russian seller of sweetmeats, unless they had very deep and good reasons for doing so. Presumably, said Jansson—and I could see that he of course had not been taken in, but was moving in the trickery world of reckonings and whisperings and knew every step he was taking—the torpedoes presumably wished to give the old Russian one in the eye and considered it healthiest for him to lose a little money. I objected that it wasn't fair on the old man, but Janson said that he was a law-breaker who had spent the last thirty years swindling sailors and that I at least didn't need to risk much.

I was frightened.

I wasn't mean, but I was frightened for my money. With it I was to see the country, buy bus tickets, meet people in milk bars, get to the Golden Gate. Then I thought it over—with twenty dollars less I would still get to the Golden Gate.

Jansson put on an expression of not being concerned what I did; he wrapped himself round in his Peru and Puerto Rico and left me to fumble with my hands and falter with my words. I sat there in all the noise and bustle of Brooklyn and felt awkward in the presence of that carefree creature who was so familiar with ports and the sea and pantries and decks; and, inevitably, he got fifteen dollars to stake on Chesapeake Bay for the fourth race at Saratoga. Jansson dashed round the corner to find the old Russian and I went up to my room and got into bed.

The following day Jansson just poked his head round my door in the morning and said that he had a receipt for our bet with the Russian, and that I was to keep quiet about it as it was all illegal. Then he disappeared. He had told me that he had to go up town to Manhattan to meet a lawyer about his thumb.

I spent the whole day trying to appear unconcerned. I thought of things other than my money. There was an old Spanish mate living there by virtue of being with a Norwegian ship and that morning he was ill. He could not eat his flakes and sliced banana in milk as he usually did, but just sat there with his head in his hands. I disposed of an hour by telling him to get himself to bed and going up with him in the lift and seeing that he got to his room. Sleet was falling outside, and I fought my way through it to the laundry with a bundle of dirty clothes, and after that there was just the afternoon left. I went up to the top of the Seamen's Home and sat there playing patience and looking out across the tower of the Williamsburgh Bank and through the snowflakes towards Canarsie. I felt ashamed because of the way those damned fifteen dollars were unnerving me. I felt mean worrying about money and that in the house where Heyerdahl had sat with chart spread on his table working out his Kon-Tiki dream. Here, in the afternoons sometimes, it had struck me how rich life was. That was when I sat listening to the talk of drowsy seamen rolling cigarettes in their great hands:

"I haven't seen him since Valparaiso, a spindly little titch. . . ."

I was in Brooklyn, seething and noisy, and there was someone somebody hadn't seen since Valparaiso, a city far-removed from the drab everyday, so deep in the realm of adventure.

There were several minutes round five o'clock when the snow fell in a thicker and thicker blanket of flakes and I forgot my fifteen dollars. There wasn't a sign of Jansson. For all my anxiety there was one fear I never had: it never struck me that I ought to have asked Jansson for a receipt for my stake. His thumb, his obligingness, his use of the waste-paper basket—in everything there was something fine and genuine about him that made me feel I could trust him.

I didn't have the dinner at the Seamen's Home that day, for the simple reason that I was too agitated to do justice to the pork sausages, and also I was already reckoning on having lost my money and how I should have to adjust my way of life, not just for the next week, but for a long period ahead, in order to make up for my extravagance. I lay on the bed in my narrow room and looked at the furniture: a desk, a chair by the window, a bedside table.

At eight o'clock I got up, put on my shoes and went out into the swirling clammy snow, crossed the street and made for Hanson Place, then into the Long Island railway station on Atlantic Avenue. The hour had struck. The *Herald Tribune*'s "early bird edition" was out, the next day's paper ready four hours before the previous day was over. Those taking the train to Long Island jerked their copies with systematic impatience from the great piles on the newspaper stand; the attendant had his hands covered with black and violet printing ink from the weeklies. I got my paper and slowly seated myself on a bench in the waiting room. I found my way to the sports pages, saw a big picture of galloping horses whose hooves were sending sods flying all over the block, my unaccustomed eyes moved down the lists of results till they read:

"Fourth Race: 1: Chesapeake Bay, ridden by Arcado. . . ."

When I walked out through the heavy station door by which I had entered two minutes previously, it was into a different day. My nasty agitation had grown and my greed with it. Before I had just been afraid of losing fifteen dollars; I would have given anything to have had them back. Now my fear was that my winnings might be too small. I knew that there was no point in looking to see what the totalisator had paid on Chesapeake Bay, as I was betting with an illegal bookmaker and quite different odds. Before my desires had been humble enough: to avoid loss, to win just a little, say the next week's rent. Now I was in a flurry in case I shouldn't make enough.

I was in a state of exaltation when I returned to the Seamen's Home some minutes later. I had to go and sit in the café and gaze at the television screen to keep myself in hand. There was a girl with some dolls doing a stupid sort of Punch and Judy show. She had a neck-line that plunged below the TV screen. I couldn't find Jansson anywhere. I stayed up till midnight, hanging about the door, running across to the Greek's bar to look for him, until in the end I was exhausted and went to bed.

He came in next morning before I was awake. He had got hold of Solveig, the Norwegian girl who did the rooms, and borrowed her key. With a great assumption of solemnity and grave expression he slowly counted out 240 dollars on to the table beside my bed.

The bookmaker had given 16-1.

That evening Jansson and I packed our kitbags and deposited them in the luggage room of the Seamen's Home. Then, each wearing a new suit and carrying a new leather case, we went up the Hudson to Lake Champlain deep among the Adirondacks beyond Plattsburg. I can still remember the heavy soft armchairs in the foyer of the hotel, the thick carpet in my room, and how I opened the window and looked out into the night above the woods. There was television in the room and a wireless on the bedside-table, and, outside, the night was filled with sound, small melodious sounds, the rounded sounds of streams and wild things and crickets.

I didn't see much of Jansson during that period. We perhaps had a few meals together. He went his own way. It transpired after a time that he had gone to that place just because he had worked in a neighbouring hotel two years previously and there found a mulatto girl whom Jansson with the thumb considered unsurpassed. But she had left. He managed to make other arrangements. I learned how to fish from an old boy who hired out boats down by the lake. But most of the time I just rowed about, went ashore and sat on a fallen tree in the woods and smoked and did nothing.

It was while I was being shaved one morning in the saloon round the corner that I came to realise where I was, and it was then that the West came over me. There was a map, a cheap tourists' map with silly drawings, hanging on the wall beside the chair on which I reclined while the barber soaped my face, and there I saw our hotel. And then all the names round: Fort Ticonderoga, Saranac Lake, Fort William Henry, Cooper's Cave, Kent-DeLord, Sacandaga. As the razor slipped over my cheek I realized that I was right in the middle of the West, in the romantic "West" of my boyhood. And that I could borrow a bicycle and go off to Cooper's Cave in which Alice and Cox were shut while the last of the Mohicans tried to help them, and that it was all thanks to Jansson with his quiet ability to deal with sharks and the way he had invested my fifteen dollars in Brooklyn, desolate Brooklyn with its hellish clamour.

That day I rowed up the lake until I was out of sight of the hotel, pulled my slender boat up under the bushes on a headland and lay there and kept watch, half expecting a birch-bark canoe to come swiftly and silently round the next promontory, paddled by grave Redskins.

2

WELCOME TO TOMBSTONE

It was past nine o'clock when I arrived, and it had been dark for a couple of hours. I had wound down the bus window now and again as we went along and knew that the desert night was cold.

It had been a wonderful day. We had got out in Skeleton Pass just across the New Mexican boundary to look at a cairn erected in memory of the capture of Geronimo by the cavalry there. The afternoon had been blazing hot; in Douglas we had scarcely been able to walk the ten yards from the bus to the cafeteria because of a whirlwind that came swirling across the dusty plain. It had an empty whisky carton with it which spun like a top all down the broad asphalt street through the town, and when the girl at the coffee counter had run to the door to shut it properly, the wind had lifted her skirts so that we saw she had round garters with rosettes on them. Afterwards, when we were groaning up out of Bisbee's mining canyon with gears singing, rain had overwhelmed us.

Now, in Tombstone, the night was dark blue and made you feel solemn.

I watched the bus swing round the corner and heard it disappear into the stony desert. It left me standing with my suitcase on a wooden sidewalk; I could hear the faint sound of jazz music coming from somewhere. To the left was a closed drug store. The wall beside me was white and mute, but a funnel of light was falling on to the road from a doorway on the corner.

A man emerged from the shadows round a telegraph pole and came towards me.

He was an old fellow with white wisps of hair beneath his hat and a sunken chest. He wore only a torn shirt which hung over his trousers, and he scratched at one shoulder with his hand under the shirt as he stepped towards me.

"Do you need a room, Mister?"

I hesitated. I ought to have a look at it first. But I had no excuse for waiting before making up my mind, and so said "Yes."

He tried to lift my heavy suitcase, but his fragility made me afraid and I told him to give it to me. Then I put it down again at once and asked where I could get something to eat.

"The bar's open there," said he and pointed towards the light.

He walked ahead of me into Crystal Palace, and I smiled at his assumption that I would follow.

When I came in he was standing there, small and pathetic, with his hat in his hand, saying:

"Gentlemen, there's a stranger come to town."

Crystal Palace was an enormous place. Parts of it lay shrouded in darkness. On the left was a bar that ran the whole length of the long wall. I had never imagined that a bar could be so long. It disappeared into the darkness. Right at the end I saw a platform, and on it a piano. To the right was a line of stalls with tables and leather seats.

In one of the stalls sat a number of men with broad-brimmed hats over their eyes, and it was they whom the old man was addressing. They looked at me and beckoned to me and began moving up and making room on the seat. One came over to me, a tall pale chap in blue dungarees and high-heeled boots.

"Let's first hear what you're going to have," said he. He walked across to the bar and shouted in towards the darkness:

"Judah! Judah! We've a guest."

Judah emerged from the gloom behind the bar, slowly drying his hands on a towel he had tied round his stomach. He was a small elegant man of perhaps seventy. He wore a gaudy shirt with horizontal stripes and a tie with a large tie-pin stuck in it. His long grey waistcoat, which was shaped in at the sides and had small diamond buttons, was spanned by a thin gold watch-chain, and a large old-fashioned breloque dangled from the pocket.

Everything about him sparkled. He was a reflex, emitting sharp rays from his smiling gold teeth, from his unframed spectacles, from his rings, from his watch-chain and waistcoat buttons. I had to exert myself to look past all that metallic glitter and see his face: it was the brown and furrowed face of an old man, with wrinkles forming a pattern of squares on the nape of his neck where the skin was stretched like old ox leather when he turned to face the shelves where his bottles stood and pondered what he should give me.

"Sorry brother," said he, "I was doing lessons with my grand-daughter, Ysabel, in there. So you came with the bus. Where from?"

"I left El Paso this morning."

"You'll be needing something, then."

"I only want a hamburger or a sandwich and a glass of beer."

"I've no sandwiches here, but I'll send the girl home to her mother and get some. I've beer enough to last a lifetime, if you stay that long."

I said that it was too much bother to send the girl, but she had already gone. The shelves looked very tempting. I had scarcely expected to see Pernod and Armagnac or Drambuie out there in the desert. But I didn't want anything but beer, and old Judah poured me out a large glass of Blatz most tenderly.

A great peace descended upon me as the froth subsided and I settled myself in the leather seat and stretched out my legs under the table. The company required nothing more than short greetings. The tall pale one had sat down opposite me, and Judah was standing behind me holding a glass of water at which he kept sipping. I was conscious of a feeling of well-being after such a day. I remembered my morning coffee in the hotel at El Paso. After it I had walked across the street and eaten bacon and eggs and bought a cigar and stood leaning over the rail watching the crocodiles that crawl about in the centre of the market place. A cheerful negro had cleaned my shoes and told me about a bull fight in Juarez on the Mexican side which he had been to see the day before. At times he leaned backwards and spluttered with laughter and somehow his gaiety penetrated into my feet. When feet are too hot or too cold there is nothing so good for them as a cheerful negro cleaning your shoes: he gives them fresh courage to keep going. Later, when the heat was due with all its terror for neck

16

and shoulders and feet, I had fled from the sunlight into the air-conditioned bus and driven along Rio Grande up to Las Cruces writing down all the names of the places we passed and savouring them: La Mesa, Mesilla, Holy Cross, Rodeo, Apache, Skeleton Canyon. My day was complete: the warm morning, coffee, bacon and eggs, sleepy crocodiles, feet revived, orange juice in Las Cruces, the cool bus, view across the stone desert and expanse of sands, the dizzy sensation we felt in Skeleton Canyon when the driver told us that that was where Geronimo surrendered to the Whites, the thunderstorm in Bisbee. Now Tombstone and the beer and the leather-covered seat and the men in Crystal Palace.

Ysabel returned from home with a plastic box full of sandwiches: white bread with harsh peanut butter and ham and Boston salad. She was at the age when you don't know whether you should get up or remain seated, but I stood up and thanked her and asked her to tell her mother that I should be coming to thank her myself. Then she said goodnight, and that left the four of us on the leather-covered seat in Crystal Palace.

Two of them I thought looked pretty peculiar. Of one I could only see a bald pate. He sat crouched over the table rocking his body gently to and fro. He was very loquacious, and when he wanted to ask me where I had been before I came to El Paso, his eyes fought desperately to get on to me and he had to screw his whole trunk round to look at me. I realised that he had rheumatoid arthritis. I looked him in the eye as naturally as I could: the one eye was almost popping out of the corner and the other was stuck to the root of his nose. I said that I had come from far, from San Antonio and Houston, from New Orleans and Memphis and Atlanta and Charleston and Richmond and New York, and really from Europe, from Sweden.

"I'm Swedish too," said he. "From Southern Sweden."

And then he laughed at that, a very hoarse laugh that lasted a long time, and the others laughed with him, and so did I, though I did not understand what was funny about it.

Opposite the cripple sat a young fellow with a long drooping moustache and incipient side whiskers. He was ashen blond and had what I took to be a dirty complexion, till I realized it was the way the light fell and his hat shaded his face and because the moustache was darker than the hair. He spoke very placidly and in a voice that echoed strangely. A cord hung from his waistcoat pocket and on it something that resembled a seal, but proved to be his tobacco pouch. Now and again he would pull it out with his left hand, with his right produce a cigarette paper from another pocket and in a flash he would have rolled a cigarette, licked the paper and stuck it down, and stuffed it in his mouth. You couldn't distinguish the movements.

They talked about the rain down at Bisbee, and I became the focal figure not merely because I was a stranger, but also because I had seen the rain. Judah walked across to the door and looked out over the rocky plain and announced that he did not think there was going to be rain in Tombstone at any rate. I realized that they did not wish to appear inquisitive, for their questions circled round me slowly and with circumspection, and when they could get no more out of my connection with the rain, they began to speak of other strangers who were expected in the town. There were the officers from Fort Huachuca. The Fort had been opened again, and the officers were to come down to Tombstone at the end of the week.

Then there was embarrassed silence for a while.

Then I said—what was the truth—that I had got off the bus just because of Geronimo and because of the name of the place: Tombstone.

Tombstone, Arizona. Tombstone in the rocky desert. I said, too, that I was going to write to my wife and tell her to come and join me in Tombstone instead of meeting me in San Francisco as we had intended, and that she was then in Natchez, Mississippi, and had a bedroom facing the river and a four-poster bed and drank her coffee on a veranda with pillars round it. Judah patted my back from where he stood behind me, and the tall pallid one who was the town's marshal, walked across to the platform and up on to the piano stool and began playing and singing: "I've worked on the railroad the whole darned day."

They all thought it was a fine thing that I had come, and the old chap who had met me first kept nodding his head. He sat at the far end of the seat almost outside the stall. He was hardly one of the party. The one with the ashen drooping moustache was called Chuck, and he told me that he had first come to the town on a foundered horse. A month before that he had quitted a job on a ranch up at Kingman and sold his car to enable him to

The story of
Tombstone—

as told at
Boot Hill.

Ormsby was one of
the stars of Boot
Hill. First Charlie—

then Red
River Tom—

then, as you
might expect,
himself.

The author
pondering the
fate of George
Johnson.

The end of

two dramas.

keep the horse, and after that he had gone riding through Arizona, but when he came to Tombstone he had to shoot his horse, and so he had stayed there.

"On that stage," said the old man leaning forward towards me, and you could see that he had taken a long time getting himself ready to say it, "on that stage in front there our High School girls dance the can-can when we have our festivals in the town here."

And he nodded violently and repeatedly.

The cripple swung his body round and managed to get his eyes directed upwards at me and asked if I had sinusitis or allergy. I answered that actually I had had sinusitis and had really never got rid of headaches, and he said that Tombstone was the right place for that. 4,540 feet above sea level. He himself was there for rheumatoid arthritis. Most people were there for something of the kind.

"Not Chuck," said I.

"Ugh, Chuck, he's not right in the head," said the cripple.

He prophesied that in a few days I would start bleeding at the nose and would feel as though the walls of my nose were stuck to the bone. But I would do best, of course, to stay two years.

"I haven't the money for that."

"I live on an early pension and insurances," said he. "Hockstaedt here is lucky, he's the marshal and earns a bit by that. His wife is allergic."

Hockstaedt was sitting at the piano still singing about how he had worked all day on the railroad.

"Hockstaedt came from Chicago," said the cripple. "Before that he had never even seen a pair of boots like those he goes about in now. I believe he used to help his father in some business, but his wife never stopped sneezing with the hellish weather they have in Chicago, and so they came here."

It was obvious that from my contorted friend I should be able to learn most things about the inhabitants of Tombstone, but I was in no hurry.

Judah clapped me on the shoulder again and said:

"Come on, drinks on me."

He wanted to mix me a real drink, but I didn't dare: I begged to be allowed beer.

"All right, brother, we've time ahead of us," said old Judah

19

and shaved off the froth with a thin flat piece of ebony which he kept in running water on the counter.

Every now and again someone would go to the door, which was now a dark blue hole into space, and look out across the rocky plain and up towards the heavens. There was not going to be any rain, they said. Somewhere a young child was bawling, and Chuck, standing beside me, said that it was Juan's kid. I didn't ask, but presumed that Juan was a Mexican. Although Chuck was youngest of them all there, he moved more stiffly than any. Even the cripple was quicker and more agile than Chuck when he went across to the bar for another glass. In his high-heeled boots Chuck walked with his shoulders pulled back and small, short jerky steps. There was suffering in his expression and about his moustache as though his boots were too small and his trousers too tight and walking always a painful business. He wore narrow corduroy breeches which clung in permanent wrinkles round his legs. They were muddied at the bottom and thick with dust at the top where it clung in a sharp crust like armour. Having been to the bar and fetched a whisky and walked back to the stall Chuck remained standing.

"Not going to sit down?" asked the nodding old man.

"Nope," said Chuck, "I'm too stiff today."

My big suitcase, which was really a kitbag with a zip-fastener and many divisions, was standing against the bar close to the door. Judah began doing little jobs which showed that he regarded the evening as at an end. Hockstaedt stopped singing. From where he stood Chuck sent a jet of saliva out into the night. The cripple hoisted one hand up on to the bar and said in a firm tone of voice:

"One for the road, Judah. Give me one for the road."

"All right," said Judah and poured him out a nip of Bourbon. "Take that and we'll call it a day."

Chuck went out into the street and vanished round the corner. Shortly afterwards he returned drawing a little trolley on rubber wheels.

"I got it from the garage," he announced.

I set my suitcase on it, and off we all went with the old man nodding and chattering in the van. We turned left from the door of Crystal Palace and walked down the street, the same way as I had come with the bus. A white chapel gleamed ahead of us. On the right was the school. The sky was dark blue, and it ended in the lengthy silhouette of the mountains. The moon shone pallidly. The desert was naked and stretched away to the east, and in the moonlight it looked as though a thin layer of oil had been brushed over the stones for as far as you could see. Hockstaedt had lit a cigar. We stood still and looked.

"Like Golgotha," said someone.

Then we turned down the road past the chapel and had arrived. There was a painted sign: *Menander Homes,* and the old man ran inside for keys. I was given a whole house to myself, a large room with windows facing in all directions, but to reach the shower I had to go out on to the veranda. They all stuck their heads into the room and said that it looked all right, but that I had better hurry and write to my wife.

I did that when they had gone, and I had to pull the bulb on its flex over to the table to see to write. I licked the envelope down and laid it beside the bed, and then I went out in my dressing gown to the shower.

When I had dried myself, I sat for a while on the rail round the veranda and looked at the hills. It was after midnight. I heard a rustling, stirring noise in the bushes and realized that there were snakes.

3

THE *EPITAPH* AND THE CEMETERY

It was not until the morning that I saw the room properly. The sun came in through the window facing me and spread a warm yellow quilt over the bed. I had forgotten to close the Venetian blinds when I went to bed and the light flooded in over me. I was lying in a cube with four openings, none of which I had closed. Light came in from all directions.

I heard voices and gravel scraping under feet, endlessly as though a multitude were passing, and when I turned round and looked through the window by the head of the bed, which faced due west, I saw that I was living right opposite the school and that the noise was the children arriving. Two station waggons drew up and out hopped a flock of boys and girls in close-fitting blue dungarees and short-sleeved white sweaters grasping the ends of straps tied round their books.

I thought of the shower which I could not get at without going outside and realized that my home was not very well arranged. There was not a wardrobe, so my kit had to be put on the chairs and table. It would be awkward when Margareta came. I glanced into the mirror to see whether I would look decent, if I went out to the shower in my pyjamas while the children could see me. Then I discovered that by stepping out through the south window I could reach the shower in one stride, so there was no need to exhibit myself.

While the water was pouring over me and I could hear nothing, old Menander had been in with coffee, orange juice and toast for me. I sat in my dressing gown with the door open and drank and chatted with him as he pottered about in the yard. Then he told me that his wife was lying ill in their cabin and that no one knew properly what was wrong with her. She had been in bed a month. They, too, had moved to Tombstone for the sake of their health.

"Where did you live before?"

"Florida."

I pondered this for a while and thought of the palms and beaches in Florida and looked out across the stony desert outside my window: Golgotha. But when you have rheumatoid arthritis, of course life isn't any better just because you are living it in Florida.

Just before nine o'clock I took the letter to my wife and went to the post. I walked diagonally across a large empty space with one solitary stray bush growing in it and caught sight of a signboard that I must have passed the previous evening and never noticed. On it was *"Tombstone Epitaph"*.

I stood and looked at it for a while. It was the town's newspaper: *Tombstone Epitaph*. In the school the children were singing an old marching song from the civil war . . . "We're coming, Father Abraham. . . ." There wasn't a soul to be seen on the streets. It was a hot morning. I could see a long way, across to the mountains in the east and west, out over the rocks and the gravelly roads.

The *Tombstone Epitaph*'s sign extended across two large black show windows. I walked up to them, cupped my hands round my eyes and looked in. There was a writing table and a shelf with piles of newspapers, and farther in I could glimpse a handpress. I

22

tried the door, but it was locked, and then I walked back a few steps and looked at the house.

The school children had begun another song. People must be painfully neutral in Arizona, because they had switched to: "I want to be in Dixie, hurrah, hurrah!" First the marching song of the Northern states, then that of the South. I stood there holding my letter and gazed at the *Tombstone Epitaph* and longed for one of my acquaintances of the previous night to come and tell me about it. But the town might have been dead! An indolent gust, a mere breath of air, came and stirred some ice-cream paper lying on the trampled earth of the pavement.

The post office lay beyond the drug store, in the same street as Crystal Palace. It was a small place with the hatch at the end of it. I went across to buy a stamp. A tall fair-haired girl of twenty-seven or thirty was standing there, and she at once said:

"Aha, here comes the letter to your Missis."

She wore a checked shirt and a dangle of many bracelets on her thin sunburned arms. When I leaned towards the counter and looked down at the floor I saw that she was wearing blue jeans and high-heeled boots, exactly like Chuck and the marshal, Hock-staedt.

"A small town this," I said.

"Chuck was in and told me about it a while since."

For a moment I wondered whether she could be Chuck's girl, and hazarded a question.

"Where does Chuck live?"

"He and his wife live beyond the school on the Bisbee Road." That was that.

"Well, here's the letter. Any chance of it reaching Natchez by tomorrow afternoon?"

"Sure thing."

She put on a stamp and postmarked it, and I had a feeling that I ought not to run off immediately.

"What's there to do in this town?" I asked.

"Have you been to the cemetery?"

I hadn't thought of that. And usually I'm very interested in graveyards. What surprised me was that a post office girl should suggest it.

"Is there anything special about it?"

"Go and look and you'll see."

23

"Anything ever happen?"

"If you stay till next month you'll be able to see our extra Helldorado."

"Extra Helldorado?"

"Have you never heard of our Helldorado? We have a festival every year in October in memory of when the Earps and Clantons fought it out in OK corral, and this spring we're doing an extra Helldorado in order to attract a few tourists."

I gave her a serious look:

"One thing at a time, sister. Cemetery, Helldorado, Earps and Clantons. I arrived yesterday, I know nothing. I would like to know a little about the town, but I can't take it too fast. I'll start by going out to the cemetery."

"Do that. Later, Hassayamper must tell you about things some evening."

"Who is Hassayamper? . . . no, never mind. One thing at a time. Now I'll go to the cemetery."

She came to the door and stood with one booted foot on the wooden planks of the pavement and pointed out the way I was to go.

When I was a few steps down the road she called after me:

"How were the sandwiches?"

It took me a second to identify the girl who had brought the sandwiches and who was perhaps sixteen, as the postmistress's daughter; so the post office girl could not be twenty-seven or thirty, she must be thirty-seven or forty. In America I could never get over what was perhaps the most commonplace thing of all: that the mothers looked so young. I looked at her legs in blue jeans and her little cowboy boots and brown arms and said:

"Excuse me. They were wonderful. That's really what I came to say, but then you began talking about the cemetery."

Crystal Palace had not yet opened. Beside it was a milk bar which some woman or other was tidying up. I decided that I should have lunch there. Opposite was a cinema and a hot dog stall and then a large outfitters. The sun struck slantingly from behind my right cheek as I walked. I reached the end of the block and still had not seen a soul out of doors. In the next block my attention was attracted by a signboard with the legend: "Ladies' Hairdresser and Lending Library". Beyond that was a garage, and there at last I saw someone working. There was a big man lying under a car wielding a gigantic spanner.

"Haaaeeeh!" I called in greeting, putting on a bogus Southern accent.

"Haaaaeeeh!" he replied without even emerging. "So you're the Swede."

"Yes."

"On your way to the cemetery, I guess."

"Yes. I was thinking of going there. Is it far?"

"Ten minutes. When you're going farther we've always some old car or other you can borrow."

Now he came trundling out from under the car on the little wheeled trolley he was lying on, and proved to be a bald-pated man with a friendly smile. He sat there on his trolley and pointed with his spanner out through an open door in the back of the garage, and said:

"Out there you have the old OK corral where Earps and Clantons fought. It belongs to me, a bit of it at least."

"Indeed, so that's it, is it?" I replied. "I was wondering."

It was just a backyard, with some corrugated tin sheds, some rusty mudguards and a ragged seat from some old broken-up car. You could walk across the yard into the other street.

"Ah, yes," said I once again and felt rather embarrassed at finding myself so inclined to cover up my ignorance.

"I was just wondering."

"All right," said the garage owner and shot back in under the car again. "Enjoy yourself at the cemetery. Afterwards we might have a meal at Ritchies—that's the milk bar there."

After that I met no one else. The road swung abruptly to the right. The last two houses were white wooden villas, low like haciendas which they weren't. One of them was bedraggled and was neglected; on the open space in front of it stood a number of coops and cages; I heard howling and yelps and supposed that they had puppies or something in them. The other looked shut-up and genteel, and slightly decayed. *Pauvre honteux.* I even thought I saw a diving board and the handrail of steps leading into a swimming pool. Beyond the second house's garden the town stopped and I was alone with the road.

Then when I turned round to take a look at Tombstone, the houses lay tucked down in a fold so that I could scarcely see the town. But eventually I got an idea of the lie of the land. To the left was a red brick church tower. It was at the eastern end of the town. To the right, at the western end, was a tower with a fire bell. At the southern end lay the school and my little house. At the northern end lay the old villa with the swimming pool. *Tombstone Epitaph*, the drug store, Crystal Palace, the post office and the ladies' hairdresser cum lending library were in the middle of the town. Now I knew where I was.

I turned my shirt collar up over my neck to keep off the sun. The mountains ahead of me I knew were called the Dragon Mountains. Then the road dipped down slightly and when I looked back the town had disappeared. The sun was like a hot hairshirt on my back and blazed on the stony ground and the strip of asphalt. It shone so that I could scarcely see the hills, and I thought of what it must be like just to walk there without purpose. When the road rose up out of its dip, I was almost there.

The cemetery was enclosed by a white fence, and over its gate was a sign saying "Welcome to Boot Hill". Beside the gate was a little kiosk with picture postcards and coca-cola, but being the morning it was shut. I leaned over the fence and looked in. There was no earth in the cemetery—or graveyard would be the better name. Nor was there a church anywhere near. The mounds of the graves were piles of sharp-edged stones, and all that grew there were cacti and scrubby bushes.

I went in and began walking round among the tombstones. Most graves just had an ordinary iron pipe on which was fixed a bit of wood painted white with the text in black. Only one grave had an iron rail round it—the others were bare cairns without protection. It struck me that it would probably only take a couple of minutes to uncover a coffin with my hands.

There was one plank which rose well above the others, and I walked straight across to it. On it was:

BILLY CLANTON

TOM MCLOWERY

FRANK MCLOWERY

MURDERED

ON THE STREETS OF

TOMBSTONE

1881

The Professor and Margareta outside the hairdressing salon. The
Ford is, if I remember right, a 1917 model.

Margareta in the entrance to Crystal Palace. This was also the stop
for the Greyhound buses.

Beside it were two smaller crosses—iron pipes with wooden cross-pieces—the individual graves of the two McLowerys.

Adjacent to this cairn was a somewhat lower plank, though it, too, was still higher than the rest:

DAN DOWD

RED SAMPLE

TEX HOWARD

BELL DELANEY

DAN KELLEY

LAWFULLY HANGED

8th March 1884.

The sun poured painfully over my shoulders and the cairns of the cemetery. The desert and the distant mountains danced in front of my eyes. I saw a cross that threw a little shade on a piece of bare ground where there was just the smooth gravel, no chips or cactus, and there I sat down. Only then did I see what shadow it was that I sat in:

JOHN HEATH

FETCHED OUT OF

THE COUNTY JAIL

AND LYNCHED

BY A CROWD FROM

BISBEE

22nd February 1884.

I lit a pipe and thought about graveyards and how I could never put my finger on where their attraction for me lay. Actually I seldom thought about death, yet in a graveyard I felt the thrill of a sort of cheap drama which filled me with lofty thoughts for quite a while.

I remembered one day in Jutland and the breakfast I ate at Jespersen's hotel in Lemvig, I think the best breakfast of my life, and I am a great breakfast-eater and one for the sacred morning hours and don't care about lunch. It was at the naval club's premises, where there was a ship's telegraph on which you had to ring "Full Speed Ahead" whenever you wished to inform the kitchen that you required a schnapps. Afterwards I had trudged up the great hill to the station and taken the train to Harboör. The station there was deserted. There wasn't a soul in the hotel. It was like an inn in one of Gorki's books. A solitary iron bracket that once had held a lamp still sat in the wall. Then I went into an ancient shop where there was no one to serve me, and so arrived at the cemetery. There was a modern columbarium with a hundred niches for fishermen who had drowned. Above twenty-six fishermen who had been lost all on the same night was written:

God is Love.

In another corner was a common grave where the corpses washed up from the Battle of Jutland were buried:

Silent and unknown they came
Yet their hearts shall resound
On the shores of Eternity.

Supposing something happened to me now, I thought, I should just be laid there on Boot Hill, and, my passport having been sent on ahead to Los Angeles, they would write "Unknown" on the iron-pipe over me, and it would be years before a notice about me would appear in the papers at home.

It must have been the heat. It was stupid to sit and smoke a pipe in that heat. One should always leave a pipe alone till the evening.

I got up and took another turn around Boot Hill.

JACK WILLIAMS
DONE HIS DAMNDEST

A life of effort.

There was a low cairn under a bristly bush:

MARGARETA
STABBED BY THE GOLDEN DOLLAR

By walking in a zigzag I got a fine gory tale:
First:

BRONCHO CHARLIE
SHOT BY ORMSBY

Then:

RED RIVER TOM
SHOT BY ORMSBY

Lastly:

ORMSBY
SHOT

I had been there an hour. Even so I did not discover the last two until I had twice already been at the gate to go and on looking back found more crosses to examine. They were set on the lowest of the cairns. The first inscription was bitter:

GEORGE JOHNSON
HANGED BY MISTAKE

28

The other was even more peculiar:

M. E. KELLOGG—1882
DIED A NATURAL DEATH

4

THE MYSTERY OF HASSAYAMPER

I spent the days of waiting for Margareta to come in a sort of indolent routine which filled my hours well and pleasantly. I made several return visits to Boot Hill and photographed cross after cross. I used to lunch with the garage man I had met the first time I went out to the cemetery. He was called Chisholm and he insisted that he had some Indian as well as Scots blood in his veins. He was a widower and fond of company. He was also very good friends with the girl in the post office, the thin blonde with the bracelets. Her name was Mary Lou, and it was with her that I began to get Tombstone mapped. She was the mother of Ysabel, the girl who had brought me the sandwiches, and Judah's daughter. She was also divorced. But first and foremost she was the granddaughter of Hassayamper.

It was strange that no one had mentioned Hassayamper that first night at Crystal Palace. Afterwards his name cropped up in all our conversations whenever I asked anything about Boot Hill. When you saw that fine old man Judah, wrinkled dry face bent over the bar and redolent with the wisdom of age—and were then told that his father was alive! No one would actually say how old Hassayamper really was, but by my reckoning he must have been over ninety. As soon as I mentioned a name from one of the crosses in the cemetery and wondered if anyone knew his story, the invariable reply was:

"Oh yes, I've heard it, but better let Hassayamper tell it you some evening."

"Why is he called Hassayamper?"

"Don't know. Some river, I expect, where he was prospecting before he came here."

"When did he come here?"

"Well—he was here before the Earps."

So there I was again. Earps and Clantons. Hassayamper would

29

tell me the whole story himself one evening, they promised. As the cross piece on the iron pipe above Clanton's and the others' cairn said that they were murdered in 1881, Hassayamper must have been in Tombstone before that. And before that he had been washing for gold in a river long enough to be given its name.

Occasionally Chisholm and I dined with Mary Lou. Those were very public affairs and conducted with a certain pomp and circumstance. We never went about in anything but shirt sleeves during the heat of the day, so on the first occasion Chisholm warned me that I ought to put on a dark suit. I fished out a thin black suit I had with me and a fine high-collared shirt which I had bought for a tea-party in Boston the previous winter. When I got back from the shower and was starting to dress, I realized that the invitation was known all over Tombstone. Old Menander, Chuck, and the marshal, Hockstaedt, came and stood on my veranda watching my preparations while they smoked cigarettes and chewed straws. Chuck even came inside to help me choose a tie.

"Not that one. You must wear a self-coloured one."

Shortly afterwards Chisholm arrived in a new, shiny, dark-blue Chevrolet to fetch me. Mary Lou lived right in the town and we could have walked there in six or seven minutes. I got in all the same and we purred away across Menander's yard, while my three friends stood and watched till we had turned the corner. It was a solemn moment.

When we reached Mary Lou's, just beyond the episcopal church, there was another collection of people outside her gate. She lived next to the old dilapidated villa with the empty swimming pool. That was Hassayamper's home. When I followed Chisholm up on to Mary Lou's veranda which was shaded with mosquito netting I could see into Hassayamper's garden. I hadn't been as close to the mysterious old man before. Grass and bushes ran riot there. Some wild vines hung down into the dried-up swimming pool, and the steps down into it looked sadly broken and the last step was actually hanging loose.

That was a strange dinner. We dined at a lovely old walnut table out on the veranda, sitting on genuine old Colonial chairs which seemed foreign out there in the West. Mary Lou was dressed in black and had a string of pearls round her neck.

30

Ysabel waited on us. Now and again someone would come along the road and shout up to us, and we would chat with them between mouthfuls. The most inquisitive was Chuck who twice came riding up and stopped his horse by the gate and rolled a cigarette and spat most refreshingly in the dust of the road and spoke with us.

The contrast between our clothes, our solemnity and strict formality up on the veranda and the proximity of the road and the way passers-by participated in the occasion was most confusing.

We had a juicy tenderloin with baked Idaho potatoes, yet only water to drink at table. But it was water to be remembered: beside us we had a tall silver thermos-jug filled with ice-cold water that bathed and revived the body.

So Mary Lou was divorced. Chisholm was a widower; and I a grass-widower. I never knew whether it was to avoid gossip that we ate those dinners in public. The ceremonial remained unchanged when the invitation was repeated a few days later. Ysabel walked lankily to and fro between us and her room, where she sat in a chaise-longue on the veranda with her feet tucked under her, reading. Now and again she would come up and chat with us at the table holding her hands clasped behind her.

I had several dinners there.

Dusk usually fell before we got very far with the joint. Mary Lou had a rose bush at one corner of the house which her grandmother had planted, and it was enormous. At times I saw a light in Hassayamper's windows and that always impelled me to ask whether I might not go and pay him a visit and hear about Boot Hill and the Earps and Clantons, but Mary Lou just said that sooner or later her grandfather would go out into the town and visit his son Judah at Crystal Palace, and then I should hear it all.

The moon was shining one evening when we were sitting on Mary Lou's veranda. Chisholm and I were smoking Henry Clay cigars and the smoke rising from them was like the edging of some dark blue drapery; it reached the delicate carving on the roof of the veranda and then twined out into the warmth of the garden. The white veranda was as though painted with the false colours of the picture postcard. Ysabel sat in her chair reading Thomas Wolfe; she was much older than her years. Mary Lou was at the big sideboard inside getting some tall crystal goblets

31

on stands for us to have our highballs in. All was quiet and silent. Just a faint chink from Mary Lou at the sideboard; Ysabel turning the pages of her book.

"What sort of a chap was Mary Lou's husband?" I asked Chisholm in a whisper.

"A bull and a b." replied Chisholm after a while.

That was the only time we spoke of him.

That evening Chuck was at last invited up. He came riding from the direction of the Tucson highway and we saw him when he was a long way off. The moonlight glistened on his saddle-mountings and on the big buckle on his belt. We saw him up on the ridge by Boot Hill. After that he disappeared until he came dawdling past Hassayamper's house. We called to him before he reached the gate, and he pulled the reins up to his chest as he turned his horse and stopped by Mary Lou's fence. I was glad to see him, for it was becoming a bit tedious on Mary Lou's veranda; it was the third time I had been there, just another dreamy, hushed evening with moonlight over the stony desert outside and the gloomy Chisholm relapsing into more and more bitter facetiousness. The lights in Hassayamper's villa disturbed me, since I wished to know who he was and what he looked like and how he lived, and no one would answer my questions. I knew too that this was not due to there being any mystery, to anything he had done and which had to be covered up, but just to their sense for the dramatic, their knowing that I was curious and their wanting me to be fully charged with expectancy and aware of the solemnity of the moment, when the time came and I was at last sitting listening to Hassayamper.

Mary Lou called from the sideboard inside and asked him to come up, and Chuck led his horse to the back and then appeared on the veranda with his hat in his hand, very guarded and formal:

"Mary Lou, Ysabel, Chisholm, Olsson—glad to see you."

I loved the way they greeted each other in Tombstone—they were as polite as people in the drawing-rooms of Boston and the pensions of New England. They always gave you a short bow and said your name, just the name—therein lay the politeness; it was proof of their appreciation of the meeting, at the same time as it showed that they were not actuated by any sort of ordinary hail-fellow-well-met friendliness. They remembered you.

That evening, after Chuck had been given his highball, I at

last succeeded in extracting some information about Hassayamper. As I had imagined, the glamour round his name began to fade because of it.

It began when I got up and went and sat on the veranda rail and listened for a while to the evening noises of Tombstone: a distant car on the asphalt highway to Tucson, evensong in the Baptist Chapel, a baseball match on the wireless in some house in the town.

Again I saw a light in Hassayamper's house and in one of the windows I caught a glimpse of a woman, just a back and black hair, bending down and presumably taking a cigarette from a box on a table, and then disappearing; the Venetian blinds were half-way down and I only saw her long black-clad back for a second.

After a while I went back to the others and asked:

"Who's the beauty living with Hassayamper?"

That produced no exchange of frightened glances, nor had I expected any—though I'm not so sure; perhaps I had expected some such exchange of glances, for ever since walking into Crystal Palace that first evening I had had the feeling of taking part in a bad film, and whenever I turned a corner I felt for a fraction of a second as though I had walked on to a screen being watched by millions of eyes, and in the evenings when I went home to Menander's house and darkness was falling quickly, the sights round me were like a bad copy of a film. But now I was sensible and sober. I knew that there could not be anything mysterious about Hassayamper, just an old man who was stubborn and to whom they, of course, had already chattered and told him that there was a stranger in the town who was curious to hear his stories, and so the old chap wanted to key the stranger up. And presumably he was rich and could afford to keep a fresh lady companion.

"That," said Mary Lou in a tone of voice that was both indignant and amused, "is Hassayamper's fourth wife."

"She looked quite young."

"Well," said Chisholm, relieving Mary Lou of the responsibility of replying, "she's a bit over fifty, which isn't any age at all, but at least it makes her close on forty years younger than Hassayamper."

"Do they never go out?"

"Seldom. She sends out for provisions twice a week. Occasionally she takes the car and drives off for two, three days, to Phoenix or perhaps even to Los Angeles and buys clothes."

"What about the swimming pool? It looks rather dried up?"

At that all three looked slightly embarrassed, until Chisholm went on:

"She used to bathe there and swim about in the mornings. She had a black bathing dress. But the boys all happened to pass by just at that time, it was the only swimming pool in the town, and Hassayamper got annoyed and had it emptied."

"But there'll be a bathroom?"

"There are three bathrooms," said Chuck quickly, "two downstairs and one up. I fixed them once."

Chuck had no proper job, but for the last few years he seemed to have fixed most of what had gone wrong or been broken in Tombstone. He knew intimate details about everybody. Not even Mary Lou, the granddaughter, had known about the bathroom upstairs.

"Do they live alone?"

"No," said Mary Lou, "they have an old Mexican couple who clean the place and cook the meals."

"Same nationality as she," said Chisholm, and it was obvious that he didn't think a lot of Mexicans.

After that no one spoke for a while, till Mary Lou went back to the subject.

"A good many say she's Mexican. And the marriage certificate gives her name as Francis. Others say she's Indian, from south of the border. Apache."

"Apache?"

Now Chuck leaned eagerly forward:

"Exactly," said he, "Apache. There always have been Apache, a little band of them, down in the Mexican mountains. When they captured Geronimo and his last gang, people thought the Apache were finished, but there was a little band left down there. A number of them gave their children to farmers and convents, and Hassayamper's lady grew up in a convent. She told me that when I was fixing the pipes to their bath. We got talking about all sorts of things, and she said that she had been brought up in a convent. Nothing about being Indian or Apache, just this: 'I

34

grew up in a convent.' But I thought it out afterwards and I'm all for her being Apache."

Slowly and with every evening I spent there the figure of Hassayamper began to take shape. At times Judah was there as well, but he came mostly to hear what Ysabel was reading and how she was getting on at school. He was going to send her to a university, that was his dream, either to Berkeley or Southern California. Occasionally Judah would let drop a word or two about his old father, and I began to feel sure that I should meet him and hear his tales about Boot Hill. Anyway, I had plenty with which to pass my time. In the morning I used to pay a visit to the *Epitaph* and rummage in the old files and read the deaths column and the descriptions of drunken brawls. The editor had been called up; he was far away in Korea, and his wife, a silent grave girl who didn't talk much, was attending to everything. I used to drink coffee at the drug-store. Then I might walk across the street to an old museum they had in the Birdcage Theatre, which had been closed down for forty years and was full of junk: some circus posters supposed to have been painted by a Swede, a stuffed mermaid from Japanese coastal waters and at the back, behind the stage, Tombstone's old hearse, the first one west of the Mississippi to have curved corner windows. It was said to have cost 15,000 dollars in its day. There, too, lay some old shovels and pickaxes such as the prospectors had when they first came there at the end of the seventies, and there hung a large portrait of a bearded man with the look of a prophet.

That was Ed Schieffelin who founded the town. I wondered whether he was a Swiss or Alsatian or something of the kind; the name sounded like it. But no one knew. At any rate it was he who baptized the town. He had ridden out into the desert from Fort Huachuca, where he had gone with the dragoons during the Apache War. He was looking for gold or silver. The commander at the Fort had forbidden him to do so, but Schieffelin set out all the same. He was gone for months. One day when a troop of dragoons was out picking up bodies left by Geronimo they found Ed Schieffelin. He was sitting with his shovel and pick having a rest in the desert.

"What are you doing, Ed?"

"Prospecting."

35

"Where?"

"Here in the hills. Everywhere in the hills here."

The dragoons looked around them and thought of the scalped bodies they had seen and of the Apaches lying in wait and sending death from behind the rocks. Then one of them said, slowly and emphatically:

"All you'll ever find here is your own tombstone."

Some days later Schieffelin found silver out there among the rocks near where I was living. He struck a bit of rock with his pick and saw the gleam of the metal. He fished his only liquid asset, a silver dollar, out of his pocket and pressed it into the gleaming stuff. The coin left a perfect impression on the stone. Silver all right. He rode into Tucson to register his claim. When the clerk at the desk asked what he wished to call it, he remembered the dragoon and said:

"Tombstone."

*   *   *

One morning when I woke up my nose was bleeding. It was a thing which seldom happened to me, and so I was more surprised than disquieted. It couldn't very well have been due to over-exertion, because for the best part of a year I had lived a carefree life and had exerted myself not at all. I decided to take things quietly and see what happened. I spread my mattress on the veranda and lay there quite still in the sunshine for the best part of the morning, but my nose just went on bleeding. Menander was not the one to discuss such matters with, so I went up to Judah who was just opening Crystal Palace in anticipation of the arrival of the first thirsty motorist of the day.

"It's the height above sea level," said he, when I wondered what was causing it. "High, dry air. That's what people are here for. It's useful. Nose bleeding only does you good. Makes you feel fine. Have a beer and cheer up."

"No thanks, it's a bit too early."

I realized then that Tombstone was like Switzerland, though it was nothing but rocks and cacti. I thought of the suppurating sinus I used to get in November in Stockholm and all the mornings when I used to have to go to the clinic and see all the old men in their big furs sneezing and winding bandages off their chilblains

36

before going in to the doctor. Perhaps I should get rid of it in Tombstone, if I lived quietly and breathed properly and ate well.

That day I started a sort of cure, which I worked out for myself with great seriousness and which only differed from the way I had spent my days there previously, in that I now lay down on my bed for a bit in the afternoons with all four windows open and inhaled the cross draught; that made me feel wonderfully fresh when I got up and began wondering about dinner a while later.

It was during one of those afternoon rests that I began thinking about why I remained in that inhospitable countryside with its tormenting sun and lived in that absurd room with its four windows and inconvenient shower. I realized that it was because I was still hopelessly romantic, that it was a residue of Red Indian stories and film matinees deep down in my subconscious which had brought me there and kept me pinned to Crystal Palace and Boot Hill. Every evening I sat and gazed at the old bullet holes in the ceiling above Judah's bar and once, when I had said to Chuck that perhaps there weren't any coffins at Boot Hill, and he had offered to go there with me and bang a bit of iron through the stones to see if there would be an echo from a coffin, and perhaps even take a look at one, then I had shied off and not wanted to go. In part the idea itself was too gruesome, then, perhaps, there would not be any echo from a coffin, and even if there were, I still could not be sure. I just did not dare put my imaginings to the test.

5

MARGARETA ARRIVES

The first thing Margareta did when she got to Tombstone was to go to the hairdresser's. She arrived late one Thursday evening, and I borrowed Chuck's ricketty little lorry and drove to Bisbee and waited for the bus there. It came, shining, quiet and powerful, and I went in and woke her gently and took her luggage and heaved it on to the lorry. She went straight off to sleep again and never noticed that I was almost unable to get us up the hill out of

37

the canyon. We reached Tombstone three-quarters of an hour after the bus.

In the morning she went to have her hair done. She would do nothing till that was accomplished.

Rather naturally I did not know the ladies' hairdresser, he was in fact almost the only person in Tombstone I had not yet met. I went to his salon about eleven to fetch Margareta for lunch, and found the two of them sitting chatting across a table.

He was a strange man. He was short and slight and had a white goatee beard. It was no Wild West beard like that which graced the jowl of the old man in the house next to Hassayamper's, who kept wild cats and young jaguars in cages, but a very European little beard, the beard of a French statesman. He wore a white overall with short sleeves. His hairdressing business was strangely combined with a lending library, and it was into this and its reading room that you came first. The actual hairdressing salon lay beyond. He attended to them both. When I entered to the brittle clang of a bell fixed on the door, he was sitting in converse with Margareta about Anais Nin. I joined them and we talked about books and each other. He told us that he had been professor in American History somewhere which we were informed was just about the worst imaginable place for sinusitis and allergies. His wife and daughter were allergic, and he had sinusitis. He had come to Tombstone with wife and daughter to get well, and in two days he had discovered what the town lacked: a ladies' hairdresser and a lending library. When the girls wanted their hair done they used to go to Tucson, and neither they nor the young men read books. His salon supplied a cultural need. He had taken a correspondence course in hairdressing, and on the walls hung colourful certificates to the effect that he was an authorised ladies' hairdresser and doctor of philosophy of Harvard University, that he had read criminology at the University of Chicago, economics at Southern Methodist, and much besides. He had got books by the thousand. He had whetted Tombstone's appetite with Wild West stories and Jack London, and finally introduced Hemingway, Wolfe, Capote, Nin and Dorothy Dix's books of advice on etiquette.

There could have been no better proof of the position I had attained in Tombstone, than the fact that we were now faced with the problem of how to allocate our first few evenings. We both wanted to accept the hairdresser's and professor's invitation to dinner, yet it would look bad if I did not first take Margareta to meet the boys at Crystal Palace. They would be expecting it and would undoubtedly dress up for her that first evening. The following evening was earmarked for dinner with Mary Lou. The professor's kindly invitation remained unanswered for a few seconds, while I reviewed all the possibilities and thought how you can never join a community without becoming caught up in situations and obligations that make it impossible to do as you like without being ruthless. In this case, it was incumbent upon us not to disappoint the boys at the Crystal Palace of their evening, leaving them like people who have dreamed all day of seeing a play only to find the "house full" boards out when they reach the theatre.

It was then Friday, so I asked if we might go to dinner on Sunday. It was then that the Professor said something that rather took us aback:

"I'll come and fetch you in one of my cars."

If he did run to two cars, it was a little out of character for him to draw attention to the fact. I did not like that little manifestation of vanity, but supposed that it and the beard went together.

All went according to programme. That first night we had dinner at Menander's and then went across to Crystal Palace. The boys went up on to the stage and sang, and Chisholm proved to be a bit of a pianist. At Mary Lou's the following evening all was fit and proper: heavy silver, quiet mild night, desultory conversation on the veranda and the smoke of our Henry Clays wreathing past the girls' heads into the deep dark blue.

Sunday was hot and we just sat on Menander's scorched lawn and sunbathed for a few minutes at a time in the intervals of going indoors for a shower. Margareta had been out to Boot Hill, where I had scared her by doing as Chuck had suggested and thrusting a piece of iron piping into a cairn and producing a dull, echoing sound from a coffin.

The Professor came as arranged shortly after seven that Sunday evening. He arrived in an old T-model Ford, gleaming and polished as if it had come straight from the factory. It had high, slender wheels, and a newly varnished, glossy black hood. It was a 1918 car.

The Professor had a hacienda called Kalawao, which we said was a pretty name. He told us that it was the name of the leper colony on Hawaii, but the colony was most beautifully situated and that was why he had taken its name. Kalawao was a rambling white building said to date from the 1870's. It had been built by a German, a chemist from Heidelberg, the Professor thought. He had lived there long before Schieffelin came and had prospected for gold and silver, without ever finding any. When Schieffelin made his great find and took out a claim on Tombstone, the German shot himself out of sheer chagrin. Since then the house had been added to, rebuilt, repaired and modernised, so that it was difficult to find anything that was more than ten years old.

When we arrived, we drove into a long, low building that for a moment I thought was a hangar, or it might have been a swimming bath or a skittle alley, or perhaps an indoor rifle range. It was a simple affair, an ordinary rectangle with adobe walls and corrugated iron roof.

Inside, stood eighteen T-model Fords, in addition to that in which we had come, and we realized why the Professor had spoken of one of his cars. They were arranged in two neat lines; some were closed and some were open, and above each hung a board giving its year. The oldest was from 1909. The series was not complete, which the Professor deplored, but it was impressive enough as it was: He had a closed and an open car of each year, or rather it was his intention to have that, for there were a number he still lacked. But the gaps were counterbalanced to some extent by a few mixed types. The engines were all in working order, and every tank was full. He could take any model he fancied and go for a drive. He had not been out in the 1918 model for a long time, and that was why he used it to fetch us. It was slightly unorthodox in that it had 1919 headlights, which was a pity.

The Professor talked alternately of Kant and Fords. His wife was tiny and white-haired with a youthful face, and his daughter had that sexy chasteness I had encountered all over the U.S.A., though it was more apparent on the other side of the Mississippi; the sweet little laugh with one hand up at the neck, the irritatingly perfect build-up to the hips of high heels, slim legs, lace fringe of black petticoat, white patch on one knee if the legs are crossed, and then the perfect oval of the hip-line—as if the entire underpart had been obtained ready-made, black lace, high heels and all the rest of it, and the torso merely threaded on.

It was a beautiful home, with almost painfully modern art on the walls. We talked art, but only for a short while; I tried Diego Rivera's murals which were only a few days' journey away in Mexico, but Rivera was already *passé*; there was just the abstracts and then the bookshelves with Kant.

The Professor was a bit of a connoisseur; that must have been because of the correspondence course in hairdressing, perhaps of the desert as well and of the mountain sky in the mornings when he carefully selected the Ford for the day and chugged off into Tombstone.

The Professor was well-off, and that of course helped. I had already roughly mapped out the various relationships in Tombstone and discovered Chisholm's desire to marry Mary Lou, but out there at Kalawao I obtained an insight into the pattern of business associations. The Professor, Hassayamper and Judah together owned a ranch away in the direction of the Dragon Mountains. They had a foreman to manage it, and there was a large hacienda there and three guest cabins, the Professor told us. They went out there at fairly regular intervals and managed to agree about the accommodation. Judah was there the most. Being barman at Crystal Palace was just his hobby. They had owned the ranch jointly for just a year. Before that it had been Hassayamper's. The Professor did not know Hassayamper so very well, but at any rate better than anyone else who was not related to him. The three discussed and decided ranch affairs in Crystal Palace, with Judah on one side of the bar and his two partners on the other, one foot up on the brass rail. The Professor and Judah would have liked to have turned the whole ranch into a tourist pension—that was the real money-maker in Arizona— but Hassayamper, who still owned the major share, wished to continue with cattle. That was an old man's stubbornness: he did not realize that he received subsidized prices, nor did he know how cattle paid. He had owned the ranch since the 80's and bit by bit transferred a share to his son, and then another share to the out- sider professor in order to raise cash. He clung to it and his ideas. Thus, the ranch scarcely paid its way and was little more than a holiday place to which you went with a great fuss and commotion, in cars and lorries, to stay for a few days and live what you thought was the life primitive. There was electric light and a swimming pool which functioned, in contrast to Hassayamper's unused pool in the town.

It was called Lazy M ranch.

When we were sitting chatting after dinner I asked the Professor why it was called Lazy M, but he did not know. Hassayamper had named it. Presumably there was a dry, matter-of-fact reason for it, but as we drove home in a closed 1924 model the name still echoed in my mind as yet one more intriguing, mysterious thing out of Hassayamper's bottomless past.

With the Professor we felt that we had completed the encirclement of Hassayamper. He could not escape us now. We knew his son at Crystal Palace, we could look into his house from his granddaughter's veranda, and now we also had his partner in Lazy M ranch. It was only a question of days.

Margareta's arrival was all that was needed to bring about what I had waited for so long. Had she not gone to have her hair done, we should not have met the Professor; and it was through him that we obtained access to Hassayamper. One afternoon a day or two after we had been to dinner with him, the Professor drew up outside Menander's in one of his Fords, either the 1914 or 1915, and knocked at our door. I asked him in, and he came and stood in the cross draught between our four windows and asked if we would like to go out to Lazy M with him the following week and take part in the annual round-up of calves. Margareta could spend the days in the swimming pool.

We said that we would. Then the Professor asked me:

"Do you ride?"

For an instant I thought of lying and saying that I did, then I remembered the military school where I had spent a summer of torment and how I always felt giddy on a horse's back—though I do not at other heights—and how I always knew the second before I was going to fall off, so I answered:

"Not very well."

"Well," said the Professor, "they have quiet old horses, too."

I walked with him to his old Ford, and as he trod his heel on the starter he turned and said:

"And, of course, old Hassayamper will be there."

Then he vanished round the corner of the school in a swirl of dust.

I went back and told Margareta that we were going to meet the old chap, and I warned myself that perhaps there was nothing exciting about him after all. He was probably just a stubborn old

A game of faro in full swing at Crystal Palace in the 1880s. The man in the top hat on the extreme right is O'Shaugnessy, the undertaker, and Hassayamper is behind the "controller", the man with moustaches sitting with his legs crossed.

Chuck and Margareta.

The Helldorado over, Chuck drives the diligence back to the old garage in which it is housed.

man who, having once been very rich, was now just rich and afraid and plaintive, and knew nothing about Boot Hill and what lay there, at any rate no more than other people.

It was the same situation as when I had given my money to Jansson of the thumb: having made my bet I was afraid of losing and steeled myself by telling myself that I would.

The next day, with the help of Chuck, who was to go out a few days ahead of us and help castrate the calves, we equipped ourselves for our visit to the ranch. We went to the big clothing shop opposite Chisholm's workshop and bought first a black sombrero and black shirt apiece. Then Margareta bought blue dungarees and I a pair of fawn corduroy trousers. I should have liked a wider pair, but Chuck warned me that they could be very uncomfortable if they did not fit close. Shoes were a problem. I did not dare go in for high-heeled boots like Chuck had. In the first place, I could not walk in them, and with me they served no purpose. Chuck needed them, for he was to ride round and lasso calves, and when the lasso caught, he had to be able to brace himself against his stirrups in order to haul the calf in. Having no such duties, I stuck to my shoes, but Margareta bought a pair of small Mexican boots. A couple of checked shirts, a white scarf each, and we were equipped.

The last day or two before we set out were inevitably rather boring. We spent most of the time in the Professor's reading room looking through the shelves. In the evenings we paid a visit to Crystal Palace, where Judah now nodded to us quite intimately. We began to have a feeling that we ought to take some decent things with us too, for the visit was obviously more than a week-end jaunt to the wilds.

We set out on the Friday afternoon. The sun had gone in and a wide, dusty wind was blowing down from Huachuca, trailing cartons and twigs along the asphalt road. When I turned and looked back from the crest of Boot Hill it had grown so dark that I could scarcely see Tombstone. We drove with Judah along the Tucson road, saw the cairn they had built over Schieffelin's grave, turned down a narrow asphalt road that for the next hour ran through a stony wilderness, rising gently all the while. When we began to feel really sleepy, I jerked myself awake and asked Judah if he would not like me to drive. He protested mildly, but we changed over, and drove on at full speed

D   43

along the road, while the storm-blue wind enfolded us. The road took a sudden and surprising bend in between two hills like inverted tumblers, and narrowed to a confined and echoing pass between smooth walls of rock.

It was as though the storm got stuck in the pass, for when we emerged, there was evening sunlight on the other side. I leaned back and savoured the pleasure of driving thus quietly, swiftly and softly through the untouched scrubby prairie that stretched before us. My attention being relaxed, I was scarcely in time to see where we had to turn off. There was no sign-post, but some way down the road a portal had been erected forming a break in a barbed wire fence. Above the portal was written Lazy M Ranch. Both Margareta and Judah were asleep. I got out, opened the gate and drove through.

6

LAZY M

Hassayamper was there at supper the day we arrived.

He came down the big staircase to the dining-room with his wife whom we had already decided was an Apache, and he wasn't as aged as we had imagined. He wore a black suit and a shirt with a wide collar and a billowing black silk cravat with a tie-pin: it looked a bit old-fashioned, yet the shirt was of nylon, and he smelled of shaving-soap and astringent lotion.

It took a little while before you were sure what he really looked like.

On either side of his nose, from the eyes and down to the chin, ran deep furrows which could have been scars, but perhaps were merely wrinkles. His whole face was square-ruled in the American fashion by dry mountain air and a diet of vegetables, fruit juices and Bourbon whisky. His hair hung over his forehead in a few heavy, ice-grey locks. His eyes were deep-sunk and you could not see whether they were black or dark blue. There was nothing remarkable in any of that: it was a face like that of many other old Americans: chequered, dry, brown like leather and with the texture of parchment.

But the mouth was different. It was that which made his face unusual. He smiled continually, a slight smile which I could never fathom: like a knowing smile, revealing a knowledge of things, a wisdom none of us could guess at, or it may just have been a to-hell-with-everything smile with a drop of disdain at the corners. As though he were smiling in pleasure at the mere fact of being alive when by all accounts he should have been long since dead, or as if he had just got the better of everybody round about him. There was also an element of anxious arrogance in his smile: it seemed to contain at one and the same time the certainty that he was the chief person there and that everything revolved round him, and also a hint of irritated anxiety lest his being the centre of everything was under question, or perhaps it was simply that it was the smile of an old, self-assured rich man.

He walked well and easily. There was nothing to show that he was over ninety, even though his was that kind of agedness where it would make no difference knowing that he was seventy or one hundred and ten. With his heavy, ice-grey head, brown face and brown hands, the white edge of the shirt round his neck and wrists and his festive black suit the old man was somehow a finished, rounded-off personality, a personage. Like a fine receptacle of wisdom and judiciousness and of familiarity with distant and forgotten things.

We took our seats round the table, and, remembering what protracted affairs dinner with Mary Lou and the Professor had been it was striking how quickly we got through at Lazy M. We were quite a big company: Hassayamper and his Apache queen, the Professor with his wife and daughter, Judah with Mary Lou and her daughter, Margareta and I. The manager, Chisholm and Chuck should have been there as well, but they had ridden off to the outlying parts in search of some strayed cows with some newly born calves. Hassayamper ate quickly and with gusto; he liked food but obviously did not have the patience to sit long at table. He grunted slightly while he ate, and even while busy with one course he kept an intent and anxious eye on the next or on the door to the kitchen. Under such conditions there was not much conversation.

After dinner we sat down in front of the big open fireplace, in which you really could have roasted an ox; that had actually been done once or twice, which they might have continued to do occasionally, except that it made such an appalling smell.

45

There was nothing of the hospital nurse about the way the Apache queen treated Hassayamper, nor of the nanny. They moved naturally side by side. She was disturbingly attractive for her age, suggestive of a sculptured goddess of severe majesty; not altogether of this world, and yet not unthinkable in a swimming pool.

With a cigar and a cup of coffee, and some large logs from an old dismantled shed smouldering on the hearth, Hassayamper began quietly talking. First about the calves which they were to catch and brand, the ones which had strayed off and which the men were out after. Then about the fence round the pastures and about making a new corral for young horses. He even mentioned the question of Lazy M being made a tourist pension and began enumerating all the arguments against it, and then he turned to me for the first time and asked me what I thought.

I gave a conventional answer. But before I had got very far Hassayamper brandished his cigar at me, and without reference to anything which had been said during the evening, but as though prompted by an unspoken question I had had at the back of my mind ever since I first heard his name, he banged his other hand on the arm of his chair and, with an angry and indignant look, said:

"Do you know how old I am? Have you any idea when I was born? Have you the least conception when I was born?"

I replied that I hadn't, and then he calmed down and sank back into his armchair and looked at me over his cigar with an indescribably sly smile and said the date.

His sudden outburst had so spurred my imagination that he could have said 1820 and I would not have thought it fantastic; it was 1865—I thought a moment; I had met and seen people who were older.

However, I succeeded in looking amazed, with the result that his smile broadened and he gazed round approvingly at the rest of the company; evidently it was a scene to which he had been looking forward.

Once we got talking again and he had told us where he was born—in a little town in Tennessee called Loosahatchie, before the end of the Civil War—the sly and crafty look left his face and with it any hint of pettiness. The little smile remained round his mouth as he talked, but it was a gentle smile, and from the deep

46

lines on his face came a sense of peace and satisfaction which spread to us who listened to him, and his choice of words made us see the things he was talking about. Pointless old things they were: an apple orchard in front of the school mistress's cottage in Loosahatchie, voices behind the fences round each of the houses, stories about North Staters who went stumping through the houses throwing out desks and pulling out drawers, frightened negroes and what they had said and what they had thought about the railway when they saw it for the first time in Memphis. His father had arrived back from the war one evening when he himself was perhaps six months old, and by the next morning all their things were packed and they were already on their way out. His father had taken his family up to St. Louis and been on a farm in Iowa until he had a row with a Yankee hand about the war, and they had fought it out again one evening. Then they had all moved down to Texas and landed on a ranch south of Pecos. From that point Hassayamper began to remember things, and he knew exactly what he really remembered and what he just knew from having been told about it. He remembered an oak with a long table which must have had one end fastened to the trunk and at which the men sat eating in their huge sombreros. A tent was erected over them to keep the sun off, and always there was his father sitting far up the table.

Then he remembered the long drive, when they drove cattle for sixty days or more from the pastures round Nueces River across the prairie to the railway in Kansas where the buyers awaited them. Hassayamper was twelve when he went on his first drive, along the western trail to Dodge City, with 2,500 Texan Longhorns which lowed and bellowed day after day, dropped their heads and grazed and plodded along in a tremendous cloud of dust with cowboys riding ahead and behind and on the flanks, urging or calming them, and keeping them tramping along in their cloud. Ahead of them always went the cook's waggon, so that he should have the bacon fried when the others caught him up. Hassayamper's father rode out in front. Hassayamper himself had to ride with the rearguard which had to hustle along the stragglers, or shoot those which could not go on or which had worn their hooves down.

"For two springs," said Hassayamper slowly, "two springs I rode with the cattle. That must be the loveliest thing on earth,

47

riding across the prairie in the springtime. My father saw it all, of course, he always rode ahead of the cook's waggon. But I never saw a damned thing: 2,500 cattle, 10,000 hooves—they kicked up more dust than lies on the world's history. The first thing we did after coffee in the morning was to tie handkerchiefs over our mouths and pull our hats over our eyes, and we didn't remove them till supper time. The dust got in under our shirts and into our trousers and boots. One night when the cows just wouldn't be quiet but kept trampling the ground and lowing, my horse trod on a rattlesnake and gave a scream and began to rear, and in an instant the cows had gone crazy and went dashing straight through the camp, trampling the cook's waggon and killing a cowboy called Tom or something. . . ."

Hassayamper paused and there was a hush. He had mentioned the destruction of the cook's waggon before the death of the cowboy, and I could appreciate how right that was from the point of view of those days, when they drove 2,500 head of cattle up to Dodge City. In order to have food, they had to stop and repair the waggon, with straps and whatever they could lay hand on. The dead cowboy they buried among some bushes with a cross over him, and when they passed that way the next spring maybe they remembered him.

I was so excited about Hassayamper that I smiled quietly to myself. He was telling his tale from the beginning; all that lay stored there in his memory, bits might come out now and again in Crystal Palace, on a street corner in Tombstone, here by the fire—but never a tale so complete as now when he had heard that there was a stranger who had been going about asking questions about him and Boot Hill and Wyatt Earp.

Earp. Wyatt Earp.

There had been a strange sound to the name the few times I had heard it spoken across the bar-counters in Tombstone. Wyatt—like a swift heavy lash with a whip. Earp—like a light flick, a badly smothered belch.

Some spoke it with enough reverence to be noticeable in a conversation over a glass of whisky or beer, with self-evident admiration and the same sort of respect you can hear in the voices of men with childish minds, when they mention an athlete's name. Others spoke the name with a slight grimace, hinting that they were more than doubtful of the man, that they realized that others held him in respect, but that they themselves claimed the credit of not believing in him.

I hadn't delved very deep.

I knew, though, that this Wyatt Earp had been dead for perhaps twenty years, and that he had come to Tombstone when the town was altogether new. After that there were various versions. Those into whose eyes the name brought a glint of admiration said that he had been U.S. Deputy Marshal at that time, and that Tombstone would have gone to hell if he and his brothers hadn't cleaned it up and kept the cattle thieves and gamblers in order. The sceptical smilers said that Wyatt Earp had owned building plots in Tombstone and jobbed with them, and that he and his brothers had reckoned on making Tombstone their private property and that Earp had owned half the gaming-table which was in full swing at Crystal Palace day and night, cheating miners and cowboys out of their earnings.

After that the versions coincided once more, there being the incontrovertible record up on Boot Hill. There was proof that those who lay beneath the largest cairn up there, Billy Clanton and Tom and Frank McLowery, had been shot by Earp and his brothers one forenoon in the autumn of 1881, in OK corral where Chisholm now had his garage. He who had erected the board over their grave had been anti-Earp, one of those who looked askance and sneered at him, for he had written of the three, "Murdered on the streets of Tombstone". The Professor, for example, was anti-Earp, but Chuck and Chisholm and Mary Lou spoke well of him. Judah grunted: he was presumably very doubtful of the man, yet had no definite views about him. It made no difference that Earp was dead; they had all formed opinions about him with as much definiteness and seriousness as though he were still alive and might walk into Crystal Palace any day, so that they had to be clear in their own minds how they would receive him.

I knew too from my studies on Boot Hill and in the old files of the *Epitaph* and from various conversations, that the circumstances under which Earp had left the town were in dispute, and that none properly knew how, why or when he had left Tombstone. After they had sent those three to Boot Hill, one of Earp's brothers had been killed and another gravely wounded in some shooting affray. Then one day Wyatt and his two other brothers had ridden out of the town without a greeting for anyone or a word of goodbye, and had never come back; but during the next couple of years people kept finding in the Dragon Mountains and beyond Huachuca the bodies of cowboys and cattle thieves who could have been suspected of having taken part in the murder of Wyatt's brother. Wyatt vanished, but he left a streak of blood behind him.

Judah worked half an old stable-door on to the fire and stirred it up, and Hassayamper, speaking very slowly, said:

"I was the only one out here who had met Earp in the old Dodge City days. That's to say, I only saw him. I was just a kid then."

With that he thought he had said enough for one evening. He started preparing to go up to bed: struggled up out of his chair, stood irresolute and trembling for an instant until the Apache queen put her arm through his; then they said goodnight and walked together up the big curving staircase to the upper storey. She had not said one word since dinner.

Margareta and I had an annexe to ourselves. There was a large room with one wall of glass, a bathroom, two gigantic beds, and a desk. First, we went for a walk down the road, past the corral where some sleepy but sociable young horses appeared out of the darkness and stood at the fence to snort at us. They were just dark bodies of inquisitive amiability; we could not even see if they were bays or blacks; the night was too compact. We thought we saw an old man some way off in the darkness standing stock still and that he might be ill, but when we got up to him it was a cactus.

The next day was both trying and uneventful. We walked about in the heat feeling that there must be lots of things of the utmost interest, yet all the time we were longing for the room with the wall of glass which you could wind down, where we could have dozed in pleasurable sloth. We sat on the rail of the corral watching Judah and Mary Lou leading a foal round and round and talking to it all the while, as a first step in its education. It was deadly boring. The atmosphere at the swimming pool was rather oppressive, because the Apache queen never spoke and just sat there like a statue smearing herself with cream and looking displeased whenever anyone came out of the pool and wetted the surround.

We joyfully greeted the afternoon breeze and some clouds over the Dragon Mountains. With dinner came the night, equally massive and mighty, and encircled Lazy M; we all took a few drinks and were in high spirits, and when we seated ourselves round the fire the atmosphere was one of well-being, repletion and epic, and Hassayamper started off again even before the coffee was poured out:

"Yes, I knew Wyatt Earp when he was in Dodge City, and I remember when he collected the money for Katie's piano—that was one of the best bits of work I have ever seen in the West."

7

KATIE'S PIANO

"Earp," said Hassayamper, "was just about the most stylish chap I've seen. He was tall and fair-haired with a big moustache, and it was a mystery how he managed to be so neat and well dressed in the West, as he always was. He always wore black. He had a black half-length coat which reached almost to his knees, and always the same sort of large black Stetson on his head. Large black cravat. Black trousers, black boots. The suit wasn't always the same. He had a whole collection of them, but they all looked alike. I can't remember him ever changing. In that get-up he never looked the sort of person he really was—he looked like a gambler, a card-sharper. Earp gambled a lot, mostly faro and poker, but he was honest; and it was a great mistake, if I may call it that, that he should have worn those clothes."

The Professor cleared his throat and stirred his coffee, but Hassayamper paid no attention to that.

"Earp was one of those who were known all over the West. It was strange how a man's reputation spread. There was never anything about him in the papers; you heard it in the evenings when camp had been made and the cattle were standing snorting and being restless and the cook was dealing out the bacon. Somebody would begin telling a tale about them—about Earp, Wild Bill Hickock, Bat Masterson, Tilghman, Man Clemens. Then there would be discussion and usually quarrelling about which of them shot best, and there would be as many opinions about that as there were cowboys. They talked about them as people nowadays talk about baseball players. None of my companions in those days could shoot particularly well or wanted to, except when they were tight; but they talked about crackshots and expertness in shooting as though they were connoisseurs. Just as people who can't play baseball discuss pitches and homeruns. When I first met Earp he didn't yet have the reputation of being the best shot—he didn't get that until after Tombstone, and then he never cultivated it. No, people talked more of Hickock. But Hickock was old by that time; the devil knows if he hadn't already been killed up in Deadwood before I was born—or at any rate grown-up. Wild Bill was shot in the back when he was sitting playing poker, and he had three aces and two eights in his hand. That's known as dead man's hand because of it, and I suggest that you, gentlemen, look out if you should ever draw it.

"Wyatt wasn't quite thirty when I rode with my father on that first drive up to Dodge City. No one then mentioned him among big noises. Wild Bill Hickock was considered unbeatable as a shot on the right side of the law, and Clemens and Dave Roudabaugh as the cracks on the wrong side. Now I ought to make it clear that I actually belonged on the wrong side of the law too. It was this way: We lads from Texas were months on the trail driving cattle north up to the railway—it ended at Ellsworth one year, perhaps at Wichita or Dodge City the next. The railway was creeping westward and the Texas boys altered the trail for the cattle accordingly. Now the Texans were out on the trail for several months, two at the least. When they reached the railway the foremen sold the cattle and paid the men their wages. In railway towns there was only one street which counted. In it there wouldn't be a single building which didn't contain a bar, a shady hotel or a gambling-den, and in all three places there would be women. Things were pretty hectic.

"There was the further fact that most of the cowboys from Texas were old Southern State soldiers, like my father, and the people the railway employed to buy up cattle or who were sent to keep order at the cattle-yards were old North State soldiers. The result was that everybody was ready to fly at everybody's throat right from the start. I went on three drives with the cattle and all the last week out on the prairie the Texas boys were nearly beside themselves with excitement. It wasn't just because they had been lying out for a couple of months, life down in Texas wasn't so varied either—just catch calves, gather in cows, keep watch. . . .

"When we were getting near the cattle-town and there were perhaps five or six days to go, they talked of nothing but which women they were going to have when they arrived, and what a licking they were going to give the Yankees when they met them in the bars. And up in the cattle-town the North Staters were saying the same. People were tough in those days. They fought over anything, the women were just an excuse, and once they had got going and were really fighting, it was nothing to pull out a revolver and shoot someone.

"In my time I have heard so much nonsense talked about how you shot with a revolver in the West in those days, that I'm surprised my ears haven't dropped off. I have heard stories of chaps who shot so darned quickly that they didn't need to aim, they could shoot a fly at a hundred yards even when holding the gun at their hips. That's ludicrous. I have seen the best revolver shots there have been to see in this country and none of them shot from the hip. They took their time and aimed. Naturally not a long time, but such time as they needed. I never saw them shoot except with their hand level with their eyes and never without taking proper aim.

"Then," went on Hassayamper, who had obviously got on to a pet subject, in fact in his eagerness he had got up to demonstrate with the sugar-tongs how you did shoot, "then there were a thousand different ways of filing the trigger or the bead so as to have everything exactly as you wanted. Earp always had his pistols in holsters on his thighs, quite far down for he had long arms. Wild Bill, for example, had one revolver in his belt right in the middle of his stomach, stuck into his trousers, and the other under his left arm. There were all sorts of variants. Roudabaugh carried his pistols crossed on his chest, presumably because he had been in the cavalry and that was the regulation way of having them.

"I have seen, and heard of, many who were supposed to be wonderful at all sorts of acrobatic shooting, ones who could shoot backwards over their shoulder if they held up a mirror and looked in that, and all sorts of things like that. But I have never seen such a trick-shot get away with it when things were in earnest. He who came off best then was the one who got his revolver up quickest, aimed calmest and shot first.

"And that brings me to the really interesting thing. It concerns Wyatt Earp's reputation. I never saw, nor did I ever hear of his taking part in any shooting match such as the big aces used to get up for fun or a wager when they did happen to meet. He would stand and watch, being interested, but never take part. So nobody really knows how good he was, but I guess he wasn't in the same class as Tilghman or Hickock or Roudabaugh and the others. He was one rung lower—naturally he shot better than the rest of us mortals, but presumably he couldn't compete with those others.

"Yet he was reckoned one of them. And you won't realize how remarkable that was, until I tell you that up to Dodge City, up to that day at OK corral in Tombstone, he had never killed a soul. It sounds extraordinary, but it's true. He had never killed a person! The others had mysterious notches on their butts which everybody believed denoted the number of people they had shot. Roudabaugh had sixteen on his at that time, and he himself always said that he didn't count niggers and business men—but he was a drunken devil. Earp had no notches. And he had admittedly never killed anyone.

"And more remarkable still—he had scarcely ever fired a shot."

Hassayamper took a strong pull at his tumbler of brandy and gazed dramatically into it to emphasize his words. They hung there in the air with great effect.

"He was just so darned quick-fingered," said Hassayamper after a while.

"Earp came from somewhere in Illinois, from an industrious, religious family. But his father had the madness in him: he must go West. It wasn't enough for him to bring a bit of land into cultivation, getting it free and without mortgage—after a bit he had to be off farther west again. I don't know if Wyatt was born in Illinois or Iowa, at any rate it wasn't long before he and the family were in the San Bernardino Valley in California. He did a correspondence course in law for a bit, because his old man wanted him to study; but then he slipped off on his own. He drove a diligence across the mountains to Arizona for a while, then he ran a haulage-business when they were building the railways up in Wyoming and made a pile transporting sleepers. After that he turned buffalo-hunter, and then he made money—ye gods! he was supposed to have been one of the richest men on the trail on those days. The buffaloes? Well, it was brutal and they ought to have kept out all the amateurs who just wounded without killing or who shot and didn't do anything with either the meat or the skin. But if there was to be any civilization out here, then the buffaloes had to go so that the Indians shouldn't have anything to eat. . . ."

That sounded inhuman. The words came from Hassayamper as calmly and naturally as though he had been speaking of exterminating field-mice in order to get rid of foxes. In the faint light I could see his parchmenty face with its thousand wrinkles, and I realized that he was still living in the old days out on the prairie and on the sunburned mining passes; that his one big passion having been to get land, and to be able to keep it, he still felt that he had only just come here and that he might lose it all again; for us it was all settled and taken for granted, a possession, a bit of the roads across the desert and the streets and houses and the trees all across America, but for Hassayamper it was something he still had to guard, something that had not been there when he came, which none who had stood there seventy years previously could have imagined coming into being. Away with the buffalo. Starve out the Indians. . . .

". . . Earp was an economic buffalo-hunter; he didn't shoot one buffalo at a time so that the whole herd ran off afterwards, but chose a place where he could shoot a good day's quota without needing to move. However it was, he became rich. He could never stop playing poker. It was enough for him to hear that there was a poker school anywhere within a radius of ten miles and he would ride there. By doing that he must have been in rows, for there was always some rumpus with poker. And at the time when I came to Dodge City people went in real awe of him. Every evening my companions who had been in the city before told stories about Earp—no, first about the others, those who killed and were crack-shots. But before we pulled the blankets over us, there was always someone who rounded the evening's chat by saying:

" 'But heaven help the lot of them, if they should ever start a row with Earp.'

"And yet he had never even fired a shot.

"Do you understand how it came about? Yes, it was because he was so quick on the draw.

"According to Western usage in those days a movement of the hand towards the hip where your revolver sat in its holster was a warning. You didn't take hold of a revolver without intending to use it, and people around had to look out. I have seen a chap in Tombstone shot when he wanted to fish out a hanky to blow his nose. He kept his hanky in his right-hand hip-pocket and pushed his coat back to get at it. That was inside Crystal Palace and he had just lost 200 dollars at faro; he was standing up at the bar facing one of those he had been playing against, when he made that imprudent gesture. He was shot before his hand got half-way. I remember we laid him on the floor, and the last thing he said was to his opponent:

" 'Hell, you know, I was only going to blow my nose.'

" 'I'm sorry, Jim,' said the poor chap who had shot him.

" 'You weren't to know,' said Jim and died.

"Now there has never been any man born of woman who was so quick to get his revolver up, to draw it from its holster, as Wyatt. There are endless stories about that. Earp had been about a good deal, he was known in the railway camps and among the buffalo hunters and at poker-tables and in the cattle towns, and nobody could have led that life without getting involved in rows. But every man jack who had tried to start something with Earp had found himself looking into his revolver. He was superhuman in that respect. Before anyone saw what he was doing—his hand had been to the holster and there was the revolver aimed steadily at the other man's stomach. There was never any need for a fuss. The other begged his pardon and went his way, or grinned and said he had only been joking, or flung wildly out of the town.

"There was a rumour that Earp had a little spring inside his holsters, so that his revolvers flew up into his hands as soon as he thought of them, but that was nonsense. I asked him once in Tombstone and he showed me his holsters; they were just like any others. No, it was all in his fingers.

"He became famous that time in Ellsworth, when Man Clemens and his brother were there and began turning the town upside down. Clemens was born in London, I believe, but he had been a cowboy in Texas since he was quite small. He was a brutal chap, dirty and fat and nasty, and he shot and killed people like nothing.

At that time Earp was twenty-three, twenty-four, and he was then hunting buffalo; he had come into Ellsworth to gamble—Ellsworth was the big cattle-town before Wichita and Dodge City. That was as far as the railway went in those days.

"Earp sat playing poker all one night at one table and the brothers Clemens were at another, and the brothers became more and more rowdy, but Earp paid no attention to them for he had interesting hands all the time. In the morning, however, when the Clemens boys struck all their opponents in the face and shot the town's marshal in the chest, Earp thought things were getting too lively. He went across to the town sheriff who was standing squeezed in a corner together with the mayor and asked them why they didn't lock the Clemens up.

"That was just about the worst suggestion ever made to them. The cowboys from Texas did what they liked in the cattle-towns when they arrived. The towns lived off them, and they were allowed to harry them as they wished. The Clemens brothers were worse than any others, but nobody had ever dreamed of putting them in their place. By this time they had left the gaming-room and were standing in the market-place with some two hundred hangers-on, telling all Ellsworth to go to the devil and promising to put a hole in the first person who tried to take them.

" 'Do it yourself,' the mayor told Earp, and that is what he did. That's what made him famous. He took the sheriff's badge from his waistcoat and pinned it on to his own shirt, hitched his holster aright and walked straight out into the market-place. There was a deathly silence and Man Clemens gazed at him wondering what sort of a dude he was: Earp was in elegant black from top to toe.

"Clemens knew Wyatt more or less and asked him quite amicably to buzz off. Wyatt told Clemens to throw his rifle away and hand over his pistols, because it wasn't pleasant for anyone to sit playing cards when there was continual fighting and rowing and shooting going on around him. Clemens said: 'Obviously you're a Yankee and a damned North Stater, Wyatt, but buzz off before I singe your ears, for I have no quarrel with you.'

" 'Singe away,' said Wyatt, 'only it will make you and one or two others show the soles of their boots,' meaning of course that he would shoot them, so that they lay on their backs with their legs stretched out so that you could see the soles of their boots.

"And all at once it happed, in deathly silence, without a shot being fired. Wyatt was walking with his arms hanging at his sides, while Clemens had his finger already on the trigger and his henchmen stood with their pistols in their hands. Clemens jerked up his rifle, whether to shoot or to threaten Wyatt no one knows, and some cowboys stretched out their pistols to take aim. Yet quicker than the eye could see Wyatt had got his revolver up and was holding it pointed right between Clemens' eyes. He had no chance. If anyone shot Wyatt, it was obvious that Clemens would die that instant. Clemens looked sour, but he was smart enough to realize that his hour had struck, and so he flung his rifle on to the gravel and swore, and Wyatt took him to the mayor and he had to pay a small fine or something. His brother, who had murdered the marshal, had ridden out of the town, and of course no one knew how it had happened.

"After that coup Earp became City Marshal of Dodge City, and as he always did when he got a police job, he arranged things suitably and looked after himself. He bought himself into a gaming-bank and acquired a number of building sites. Thus he became a capitalist and had an even, steady income. Later he made an arrangement with his colleagues to pool all the money they got in—in those days the city paid three dollars for every person arrested, provided he was alive. They arrested about thirty cowboys a month for drunkenness and disorderly behaviour, and though there were four of them sharing, it still came to quite a lot of money apiece. And Wyatt never needed to shoot —he just got his revolver up and there they stood gazing straight down the barrel. Once there was a chap behind him who drew and took aim, but even so Wyatt was too quick for him. That time he was almost blamed for not having shot, but he just laughed and went and played cards with the man.

"Dodge City used to be called Hell's Forecourt before Tombstone came into being, but Earp got the place more or less quiet. He and the mayor drew up a list of prohibitions, things which they considered serious crimes and over which they would take action. They drew up their code one winter before the cattle-drovers reached Dodge City and the place was inundated with Texan cowboys. Murder and rape and the like were obviously barred within the city—with murder outside in the cowboy camps they generally did not concern themselves, but rape was considered too much wherever it took place. The city's code ran as follows: I can still remember it.

"The first paragraph forbade having horses on the sidewalks.

"The second forbade riding your horse into restaurants, bars, hotels, brothels, gambling casinos or palais de danse—that was a good paragraph for it was a nasty habit the cowboys had at that time.

"No. 3 forbade the firing of shots within the bounds of the city except on 4th July, Christmas and New Year's Day and the evenings before those two festivals.

"The fourth—fourth. I've forgotten the fourth.

"The fifth was that all who entered the city had to remove their fire-arms and hang them on racks which Wyatt had made and erected by the roads in—actually there were only two.

"The sixth paragraph was no silly one either, for it said that all who were drunk would land in jail. Now Wyatt wasn't so stupid that he enforced it, except when some really dangerous chap turned up—but it was there to be used then.

"The summer I came to Dodge City Earp was City Marshal for the second time and there had not yet been a single murder though the cattle had been pouring in for two weeks before we arrived. Man Clemens was there, but after that business in Ellsworth he was behaving himself and if anything on Earp's side, and he had bought a black coat and even begun to shave. Some youth had got drunk and tried to shoot Earp from behind, but he had had sense enough to hold his hand when Earp turned round in time; Earp had given him a box on the ear and a cigar, and the youth had ridden off home to Texas. Another muff had got himself a thrashing in the kitchen of the Alamoo saloon, where he had hidden to get a good shot at Earp, which he might have done if Earp had not happened to come in the back way to ask for a glass of water.

"One afternoon when we had been camped outside the town for three or four days and my father was busy selling the cattle, the rumour spread that now at last Earp would have to shoot and there was no knowing what the outcome might be.

"It was a strange affair.

"In the cattle-towns and mining-towns and in every hole in the West you would find in those days a woman called Katie with the Nose—or one of her establishments. She was a beautiful blonde with rather a big nose, which I personally like, and I don't think she herself was so loose. She kept saloons with a gaming-table and girls, but took things quietly enough herself. There's quietly and quietly, of course. She had once shot a man, it's true, but she was a pretty decent person. She had a business pretty well everywhere and of course she had come to Dodge City and set up an establishment there; this was a little way outside the town and so not normally the concern of Wyatt and his fellows. There was a poker table there and a faro bank and spirits and girls and music. That's to say, the music, well—the music came later.

"When she had had the saloon for a while she ordered a piano from Kansas City, and it arrived accompanied by a representative of the firm who demanded a first payment of 150 dollars. The whole piano was to cost 1,000 dollars.

"She gave the man 150 dollars, but after that she didn't worry about paying. They sent her threatening letters, but she had the piano, so there was no harm in their amusing themselves with letters. The firm's representative came out to Dodge City again to get the money, but he was thrown out rather heavily when he was incautious enough to press her, and he is said to have had a limp for the rest of his life.

"The man who owned the piano shop in Kansas City was also a large shareholder in the railway, and he grew really angry. He wrote to the mayor of Dodge City asking what sort of goddam town it was, which couldn't pay properly for the things it ordered. The mayor was scared, for he wanted to stand well with the railway and enjoy a good reputation in Kansas City when he went there in the winter to stay at Muelbacher's Hotel and live the good life a while. He realized that he would have to arrange payment for that piano, and he wasn't any happier when he read at the end of the letter that the citizens of Kansas City and other shareholders were interested in the matter, not because they worried about a paltry few dollars, but because they wanted to know whether there was any sense in buying plots and putting money into Dodge.

"Devil knows how, but all at once that piano out at Katie's

60

place had become the most important one west of the Mississippi.

"Of course there was only one thing for the mayor to do: he had to ask Wyatt for help. He didn't like doing it, for the saloon lay outside the town and there was a sort of gentleman's agreement that Wyatt and his men never went there, for the Texans had to have somewhere where they could behave just as they liked. He told Wyatt that it was of no direct consequence whether he got the money or not, it might even make more of an impression if they were to send the piano back. Wyatt enquired what percentage he might expect if he collected the money, or if there was to be any reward for fetching the piano, and the mayor gave him to understand that he should have first call on a couple of good building sites in the centre. Then he enquired how many armed men Wyatt wanted with him, and Wyatt replied that he needed only four unarmed men, four strong gentlemen who could lift a piano.

"That same evening Wyatt set out, and by then it was known that he was going to fetch the piano. The news had spread during the afternoon all over the town and to every cowboy camp round about. Wyatt rode and the four men went with him in a cart. They were not marshals in disguise nor any of Wyatt's henchmen, anybody could see that, for they were the four most notorious drunks in the town, the one who drove the cart also being the gravedigger.

Out at Katie's the place was packed with cowboys, for everybody had heard that Earp was on his way and no one wanted to miss the pleasure of seeing him shot—there was scarcely one of them who hadn't had a thump on the head from the barrel of his revolver and been chucked into clink and who now would be glad to see him out of the way. Katie's was packed with people playing cards, drinking or dancing with the girls, but whatever they were doing, they hadn't only got their revolvers half out of their holsters, but most had laid them on the counter or on the windowsills, anywhere to have them handy. There must have been close on a hundred there, as many as had been able to squeeze in, but they were frightened. They couldn't have enough firearms when Wyatt came. A lot of others lounged about outside. Almost the entire length of the road from the town was lined with people. First, nearer the town, were the townspeople who backed Wyatt, then the cowboys who didn't dare make a row or shout, but just stood and muttered.

"It looked like a funeral procession; Wyatt first with his long fair moustaches and his black frock-coat and behind him the cart with the gravedigger. When they arrived Wyatt dismounted and looked at the crowd and lit a cigar. The gravedigger and the three others didn't know what to do with themselves, but Wyatt told them to get out and follow him in.

"And that was the first time I saw him. I was standing there with my father. Father had gone there without me. He kept neutral, I can tell you that. Being a Texas man it was impossible for him to take Wyatt's side. He was a bit angry with me for following him without permission and didn't say a word to me the whole time. As Wyatt arrived I unfortunately happened to be placed just where I caught his eye and so he gave me the reins of his horse and told me to hold it for him.

" 'See to the horse, son,' said he and blew a big cloud of smoke into my face.

"What happened inside I only heard secondhand from others, of course. At first there was a deathly silence, and we stood outside wondering what was happening there in the silence and waiting for a shot. There must have been several hundred of us. Some tried to look in through the windows, but there were so many people already inside that they could see nothing, and the doors were jammed. I could not do anything but hold the horse, but I looked at my father to see whether he approved of that or not. He didn't look at me. I had a queer feeling in my stomach.

"No shot ever came. Nor did such an awful lot happen. What gave Wyatt the game was his quickness at the draw and his understanding of women and love.

"When he walked in, there was absolute silence. His entrance came as a surprise even though they had been waiting for him all afternoon. They had just passed the point when they were prepared for him to come at any moment and had begun to grow drowsy—and then he walked in. He raised his hat politely to Katie with the Nose who sat on a tall chair behind the bar, and made his way to her with the order for distraint of the piano. In his pocket he had a receipted bill in case Katie should stump up the money.

"Katie, of course, had spent most of the day wondering how

she was to fob Wyatt off when he came. She had put on her war paint. Heavens above, you saw more than half her breasts and she was so pulled in at the waist that when you screwed your eyes up, there seemed to be but a narrow streak between her hips and her bosom. She was stylish in her way.

"Now all she did was to take the paper and twiddle it about a bit, and then she asked Wyatt for his own sake to take the paper and go home again, and wouldn't he like a drink and turn?

" 'Gladly, ma'am, and thanks,' said Wyatt. 'But first I must see and get that piano into the cart.'

"Then he turned to his four removal-men who stood hiccoughing behind him, so drunk that they could scarcely keep upright.

" 'Will you gentlemen be good enough to carry the piano out to the cart?' he asked them.

"They hesitated, for all his fuelling of them on the way, but then they plucked up courage and got their straps under the piano and began bobbing and diving to get it up.

"That was the critical moment.

"Roudabaugh was the only one of the notorious Texas bad men at Katie's. Man Clemens was somewhere in the neighbourhood of Dodge, but he was sensible and had had enough of Wyatt, so he kept away. It was easy for Wyatt to see that Roudabaugh was the one everybody was expecting to deal with him, if there should be a row, and who was himself intending to wing or, why not, kill Wyatt Earp—the damned dude who went about making himself out to be a shot without ever having fired a revolver. Roudabaugh sat looking fearfully important and determined at a card table in the middle of the room. And there were a hundred other drunken cowmen besides, who would have been glad to be able to boast in the future that they had holed Wyatt Earp.

"By mortal reckoning his life wasn't worth a damn as he stood there in the midst of the crowd.

"But—Wyatt had eyes. He knew that it mattered not one whit to Katie, or anyone else, if he shot Roudabaugh—no one wanted Roudabaugh who was a rotter and a blackguard, and most of the Texan boys would have welcomed it, if he and Wyatt had shot each other.

"But then, in the thousandth part of a second, Wyatt saw that there was a Mexican sitting tucked away in one corner, a handsome chap with brown eyes, black hair, a real spark, who was twisting the strap of his sombrero round his fingers and waggling his shoulders to make sure that his coat sat properly. I don't know how, but Wyatt realized instantly what no one else had, that the Mexican was Katie's man—for the time being. I asked him many years afterwards, and he was himself surprised that he had tumbled to it so quickly. But he had seen a sort of satisfaction in the Mexican's eyes as he looked at Katie, that savoured of his being Katie's man, of his not having to work, but just lie and be industrious with her at night and get money off her with which to play poker and faro. Wyatt saw it all in a flash.

"He saw it just as the inevitable was about to happen, just as Roudabaugh and several score of the others moved their hands to get their revolvers out and stop the removal of the piano and aim at Wyatt. Naturally, Wyatt was quicker than they, even though they were all round him and had had their pistols half out of their holsters for half the day, and before anyone saw a thing, he had a revolver in his hand—just one. All the others had drawn two, and Roudabaugh had even produced a knife which he had had concealed under the table.

"Yet it was not at Roudabaugh Wyatt aimed out of all that hundred, but at the Mexican who sat there perfectly peaceably and presumably was the only one who hadn't drawn his revolver, if he even had one. Katie had told him to keep out of the way; they had scarcely exchanged a glance, still less a whisper, in public, yet Wyatt had seen through them. Katie had thought that Wyatt would aim at Roudabaugh and so be shot from behind or knocked senseless or thrown out . . . but, instead, when she looked along the barrel of his revolver she saw that it was aimed straight between the eyes of her Mexican, who had not done Wyatt or anyone else any harm, but just sat there gambling her money away and at night helping her to put up with Dodge City and the prairie and the Redskins. . . .

"When she saw that, Katie let out a yell like a wounded jackal, and that was the first sound we outside heard; naturally we wondered what the hell, for of all things we might have heard, we had never thought of a scream from Katie. None of those inside realized why Katie had screeched so horribly, Wyatt had aimed so quickly and Katie having screeched almost simultaneously, it was all over in half a second. The most amazed was

Roudabaugh; he was just on the point of shooting Wyatt somewhere in the belly, when Katie screamed and he realized that something had gone wrong.

"Katie was deadly pale and her Mexican, who understood not a thing, but of course thought that Wyatt was Katie's husband— she had a husband somewhere of whom her various lovers had reason to go in fear and trembling—had somehow managed to get under the table. Katie produced a handkerchief and dabbed her bosom, and then she asked Roudabaugh to take his hat and collect 750 dollars from her clients, so that they could keep the piano. Roudabaugh took his hat round, and men chucked money in, and when they were finished Wyatt counted it all very carefully on the bar. Then he pocketed 750 dollars, tore up the order for distraint and gave Katie the receipt. As he did that, he took off his Stetson, turned to the pianist, who had been hiding behind the piano the whole time and not yet dared emerge, and said:

" 'A waltz, professor!'

"And so he invited Katie to dance.

"We outside only heard Katie's scream and then, after a pause, the professor playing a waltz on the piano. When someone managed to get a glimpse inside, all he could report was:

" 'Wyatt's dancing with Katie.'

"We couldn't understand it.

"Well, then Wyatt came out and I gave him the reins and got a silver dollar for looking after his horse. The mayor went in person to Kansas City with the money, and a lot of people began buying building plots and taking shares in the railway. Ever afterwards the mayor used to say that if Wyatt Earp hadn't collected the money for that piano, it was more than probable that the railway would never have gone west of Dodge City, and that civilization would not have spread beyond Kansas.

"We who met Wyatt later in life, thus learned that civilization would have got nowhere, if he hadn't been clever enough to aim at the Mexican instead of at Roudabaugh.

"He got two of the finest plots in Dodge City, but he didn't choose those the mayor wanted to give him, but a part through which the railway would have to go when it was extended westwards and those he later sold to the railway people at a colossal profit."

8

EVE AND THE RATTLESNAKE

When I arrived for breakfast, the table was laden with fruit juices and ringed by empty chairs with white towels on them, for most of the others were already in the swimming pool. Sitting at the table I found the twisted little man with rheumatoid arthritis who had taken me to Crystal Palace that first evening. The Professor had driven into Tombstone and brought him out in a 1922 model, one of the fastest in his fleet. Hassayamper was being heavy and gruff with him, so I presumed that he had come on business; perhaps he, too, had a plan for turning Lazy M into a tourist ranch, or perhaps he had money. I sat at the other end of the table so as not to intrude, and the little man's eyes sought mine from their twisted angle, and he piped a friendly:

"And how is your good wife? And how is your good wife? You remember, I expect, that I'm from Sweden too, from Southern Sweden?"

And at that he laughed as long and as incomprehensibly as when he had told me the first time at Crystal Palace.

He was called Titus. It was a very odd name, but that was what he was called. Presumably his father was an Italian, or perhaps a Greek; at any rate he had had a large fruit farm in California which he had inherited and managed until rheumatism laid hold of him and twisted his poor body and he had gone to Tombstone. He had left his wife and children behind on his fruit farm beyond the Rockies and lived in one room behind the *Epitaph*'s office and printing works.

Titus appeared to have come at an unsuitable moment; at any rate Hassayamper was deliberately insolent and brutal to him and all the time on the veranda kept saying that as many as possible ought to go and help Chuck and the manager lasso the calves and castrate and brand them—he knew, of course, that Titus could not possibly go, could not even get on a horse.

Lazy M was a huge triangle whose straight sides cut across hills and cactus thickets in uncompromising directness, delineating Hassayamper's old property that he now feared might slowly slip from his grasp. The house and building were on the base line.

When we drove there, we had come in just by the western angle and cut obliquely through the territory. I had driven eighteen miles. Chuck and the foreman were thought to be at the other end of the base line, twenty miles from the ranch, where the fence formed an angle in which a lot of cows and their calves had collected.

By lunch time, all that was needed to castrate and brand calves had been packed into a waggon, and when we had eaten there was quite a little caravan lined up at the stables. There was the equipment waggon and a cook's waggon and a flat waggon with tents and awnings. I had not the least desire to abandon the comforts and leisure of the ranch, but all the others were enthusiastic and eager for the trip, and the general opinion seemed to be that it was for this that we had come. Margareta was to ride in the first waggon and I was to have a horse.

I sought for assurance that it would be an old and quiet horse, but did not dare ask too many questions.

Just before we set out, I went for the first time into Hassayamper's large corner room. He was sitting at a big mahogany table with his feet on a gigantic bearskin rug, and there were old pistols and cavalry carbines hanging on the walls and a big buffalo's head over the door. Hassayamper had spread a large map of Lazy M on the table and was to show the Professor, Judah and me where we were to meet Chuck and the foreman. In actual fact this was quite unnecessary, for Judah knew perfectly well where we were to go, but for Hassayamper it was an act of self-assertion. He could not come with us, but if he let his brown old finger roam about the map for a while, he could at least imagine that it was he who had directed and sent us.

We set out in the afternoon, by which time we had escaped the worst of the heat. I felt a twinge of fear as I mounted, a fear that had been instilled into me when I tried in vain to learn to ride, or rather others vainly tried to teach me, while doing my military service. The horse I was now given was a placid mare called Eve, who no longer let life trouble her. She was the horse Hassayamper had ridden the last time he rode, which was only two years before, and that was a comforting recommendation. She had a calm, slow walk, that was yet quite graceful, for she picked her feet up nicely. I felt slightly giddy for the first twenty yards or so, but then it passed off.

67

It was a very placid caravan. We creaked and groaned up a stony rise, then set off obliquely across a grassy plain strewn with brushy bushes, and with here and there an abandoned waggon-wheel or a tumbledown shed of corrugated iron. Mary Lou had a broad-brimmed hat turned down to the root of her nose and with the brim twisted up at the sides; it looked stuck on anyhow, but I imagine she had spent hours on it. I wondered what had happened to Chisholm, why he was no longer with us. His position on Mary Lou's veranda was almost semi-official. Apparently he was in town.

After an hour or so Margareta got bored of being shaken on the waggon, and since Eve and I were getting on well, I first took Margareta up in front of me, and then dismounted and let her ride while I led the mare. We talked about horses, and I told her about one at home called Boyar who had lived till he was twenty-eight, and that set us talking of all sorts of things that no longer existed, and then most suitably we passed an old abandoned schoolhouse with a row of outhouses. Nowadays the children all go to school in Tombstone and no cowboys with families live out there; they were all clustered at the ranch. But we imagined a schoolmistress in a checked dress coming out from the old school and us waving and riding up and talking with her, and then our little caravan winding on across the plain and her gazing after us.

Thus we rode ourselves more and more into the mood of the past; we stopped talking and just moved on towards the horizon, rocking to and fro. The sun went down behind us, but there was no being able to turn round and enjoy the sunset for half an hour; the display was all over in a few moments. It was as though a crazy pyromaniac had suddenly rushed along the length of the horizon with a tin of paraffin, setting fire to the bushes and the dry grass and the whole heavens. There was a flare of an oily red colour that swiftly subsided, and so the dire deed was done.

At about seven o'clock we halted for half an hour and had coffee round the cook's waggon, which was the domain of a toothless old chap called Hobo. He was taciturn and was continually rubbing his hands against the seat of his trousers. The coffee was as strong as it could be. Hobo had a portable wireless on his waggon and he treated us to dance-music from some dive in Phoenix with a silly, chattering disc-jockey. Mary Lou asked Hobo to get his guitar and sing for us, but he just croaked and

68

pretended to be shy and flung out his hands, but it was only too obvious that he was dying to sing, only that he required more coaxing than there was time for during a halt for coffee.

The country never changed. The only breaks were the school-house and the grass we trampled when we stopped for coffee. We reckoned on meeting Chuck and the foreman about nine o'clock. The Professor led the caravan. He rode with a sort of exaggerated assurance, a saddle-technique that suggested that he had read everything there was to be read on how to ride. Some of his manoeuvres looked as though they were not altogether necessary.

The blaze of the sunset had died down, and we rode on in cool blue gloom. I had dismounted and was again leading the mare, while Margareta rode. I led Eve a bit out of the line, for I was tired of seeing her head going up and down like a piston driving the equipment-waggon in front of us and thought that it would be nice for her to walk free on the plain. I took a line that I thought would intersect the line of the caravan further ahead. Afterwards they said that I ought to have been more careful, that they had meant to call to me, but had not managed it.

In front of me was a cairn and some spindly bushes, and I turned aside to avoid it. As we came abreast of it, Eve stopped abruptly with her fore-legs straddled, and stood trembling. The next instant she had reared up till her hooves were dangling level with my eyes, and I was aware of Margareta tumbling past my head and shoulder and hanging helplessly.

One of Margareta's shoes had been wrenched off and it still hung there in the stirrup; then Eve turned and galloped off. It was all over in a second. Then I heard the rattle and understood.

There was a rattlesnake in the grass.

Slowly we retreated, walking backwards. To be on the safe side Margareta shut her eyes, while I kept mine open to try and spot the snake. A moment or two later I saw it, as it darted in under the bushes by the cairn.

The others were laughing when we rejoined them, but Hobo just asked pertinently where the snake had gone, and when I pointed out the cairn, he took a large spit from his waggon and strode off across the grass to the bushes. When he reached them, his pace became more cautious, then he took some ludicrous little agile hops up on to the stones and stood there quite still, peering round. Nobody seemed especially stirred by the occurrence, except perhaps Margareta who felt rather sick at the thought of the snake, but she soon got over that.

Suddenly we saw Hobo lash out with his spit and spin round like a furious dog; then he stopped and held up the limp ribbon of a dead snake, so that we could see it against the dark-blue heavens.

That disposed of that, and even Eve now seemed to see it from the funny side, for when Margareta sat down to put her shoe on, Eve came and cropped the grass close beside her, making affectionate movements with her muzzle and almost knocking Margareta over by trying to get at the grass on which she was sitting. Then we moved off again. The episode with the snake appeared to have put the others in a better mood, for now both Mary Lou and the cook began to sing. Thus we journeyed on through the darkness that now was blue-black, the cacti standing ceremoniously straight along our line of march and the grass crunching softly beneath the waggon-wheels and hooves.

We reached our goal just as had been planned and calculated. The grassy plain had become stonier again and you could see from the silhouette of the waggons that we were going uphill, on a gentle rise. When we looked ahead, we saw the crest of a hill and that the dark-blue which surrounded us did not extend so far, but there was light-blue sky instead. Against this were silhouetted two horsemen, motionless and splendid. Perhaps I would have caught sight of them earlier, if I had not had my head down in quiet talk with Margareta. Now, there they suddenly were, riveted to the landscape, drawn against the sky by some mysterious hand, and the solemnity of the picture was in no way impaired by the glow of cigars that came and went under the brim of their hats.

For an instant I thought that they would dissolve as we approached, but they remained in place, and then I was able to see which was Chuck and which the foreman.

"Howdy, folks," said Chuck in a quiet voice, and not much more than that was said. Then they drew the reins up to their chins in a lordly gesture, turned their horses and rode on with us.

They had arranged a camp some few hundred yards down the slope on the far side of the crest, and there they had a big fire burning. A little enclosure had been made with a canvas screen and to this Hobo steered his cook's waggon, swung round and backed into it. Then round the fire we pitched five small triangular tents. It was all done in a sort of calm routine, the calmness slightly exaggerated where the Professor was concerned, and perhaps Mary Lou as well. All their movements were measured and deliberate; there was no discussion, no asking what was to be done, where the horses were to go, or where we were to be— everything was done quietly and as a matter of course; it was a perfect performance.

As we were stowing our things into the triangular little tent that was ours, we became aware of the most heavenly of all smells, that of roast meat mingled with the scents of night, burning twigs, grass and leather. Hobo had erected a grill over the fire, and on this he was now turning some gigantic steaks. We all dropped what we were doing and crowded round him. Judah went across to the equipment waggon and undid the straps round an old and worn but rather elegant leather case, which he eased down on to the ground with a loud grunt. This was our whisky and beer. At the other end of the canvas screen, restless Mary Lou and her girl were already busy making soda water in two siphons. There seemed to be a fixed determination that everything was to be made as pleasant as possible.

Then the foreman appeared within the circle of light.

He was called Slattery and he might have been forty-five. Five minutes with him were enough for you to realize that he had little resemblance to the general conception of the cowboy. Chuck corresponded better to that romantic picture, but Chuck was no real cowboy either, for he lived in Tombstone and, though he also mended saddles and shoed horses, he was unashamedly a sanitary engineer and a plumber as well. He did not live on a ranch. He did hunt wild cats in the mountains for zoological gardens, it is true, but his livelihood did not come from the prairie or the pass. Even so, he corresponded to the general ideal: he was stiff, chivalrous, taciturn and could roll a cigarette at lightning speed.

Slattery was quite different. He lived on the prairie. Those tents were his home for half the year or more. He spent his days riding towards a receding horizon; he would not meet a soul for weeks on end, and when he passed the empty school perhaps he too dreamed of a schoolmistress in a checked dress; he castrated, branded, hauled on thongs and ropes, a lonely life and a hard one.

71

Yet Slattery was no taciturn philosopher, but a talkative wag who never stopped smiling. His was the laugh of one who is always expecting something amusing. You could not open your mouth, before Slattery's merry eyes were on you and his mouth parted in an expectant smile. In his own mind he put everyone into some definite category and rashly attributed to them qualities that in all probability they did not possess, but which he thought would suit them; and yet he was never a nuisance. He was one of those who quickly make friends with people and at once say that this or this is typical of them. Such people live in a world of their own and are never put out by facts or what they see.

"Well, well," he laughed when I went to help Judah with the bottles, "you haven't changed a bit." I wondered about that remark for a long time, for Slattery and I had never met before.

When Mary Lou and Ysabel put the carbonic acid tablets in the siphons and began shaking them, it was apparently the funniest thing Slattery had seen for ages, for he laughed and flung his head back and laughed again and ended by thumping his hat several times against his knee.

"Well, I say," he managed to get out, when he had calmed down a bit and his features had returned to normal. "Well, I say!"

We had everything, even two big shining drums of some light metal which contained spring water that Chuck had driven off in a great flurry to fetch in one of the waggons. It was still at its original cool, refreshing temperature and we drank it from mugs as we sat round the fire while Hobo distributed the steaks. Beside us were highballs of Bourbon whisky and fresh fizzy soda water. Above us was the sky like a blue echoing vault; the fire crackled, and we all chewed and looked at each other with dancing eyes, and always Slattery was just on the point of bursting out laughing; usually, I noticed with a certain sense of disquiet, when he was looking at me.

It was one of those moments you would like to be able to seize and halt, so as to enjoy it for a week or two and let the world pass by meanwhile. But you never can. You must always be on your way. With me, such moments are always connected with food and drink, and now I found myself scraping my plate, taking a last delicious gulp of water and looking round for coffee.

Afterwards, when satiety had hushed us, we heard the cattle lowing in the hollow at the foot of our slope, as we stowed things into our tents and shook out blankets. Then Hobo began singing over by the cook's waggon. He sang all sorts of songs. One was about cattle and droving, and the owner who passed his time

In gambling halls a-playing
Three thousand cattle on the stray. . . .

Then his toothless old mouth turned to quieter, sleepier ditties, especially one about his being on the way to his last round-up. This he sang half to himself, all the while the washing-up water was heating and we were continually coming up and putting plates in the water and doing things round him. Then he poured himself a last cup of strong black coffee, got up on to his waggon and produced his guitar which had a string missing, and prepared to give us a concert.

There was one song about how girls should beware of boys, because they only lie; they invent more lies than there are stars in the heavens or sleepers on the railways. They are worse than thieves, for thieves do nothing more than steal from girls, but boys caress and kiss them, and then they vanish with their lies, and they take and steal everything. Never, never should girls hang their hearts on a youth, for he is like a young tree and its leaves wither and roots die.

Hobo repeated this once or twice, sometimes angrily, but mostly with a sort of melancholy resignation, and under the influence of his bitter songs we finally went to bed and lay listening to the heavy tramp and soft lowing of the cattle at the foot of the slope.

9

THE INVITATION

In the morning I discovered the real reason why cowboys have high heels on their boots. I had realized that it could not have been out of coquetry, for that was not a thing of which you could possibly have suspected those I had seen wearing them. I had heard that they gave purchase against the stirrup when the cowboys lassoed the year-old calves, but I had never seen that done. Now I rode out on my gentle, quiet Eve and down the slope on which the cattle were moving in a loyal, well-behaved mass, gazing mildly and innocently about them out of hundreds of pairs of benevolent blue eyes. They kicked up a tremendous amount of dust out of the dry prairie and it was difficult to see through it. Somehow the cattle seemed to be disturbed, and it was some time before I realized that Chuck and Slattery and the Professor were on the fringe of the herd searching for calves to be branded and small rough bulls to be castrated and made eunuchs and eventually turned into good fat beef.

The organization seemed rather haphazard, but I presumed that I could just thrust in and see what was going on. They got hold of a calf, then gathered round it and performed their magic rites with a long syringe, a knife, a tin with some ointment which they smeared on—a large tin, like a paint-bucket or a pail, and a large spatula which was coated and slimey. I never viewed it closer than from ten yards away, for it was not edifying to see joyous young bulls being robbed of their genitals and sexual life and most of the pleasures of existence, and springing to their feet with a bellow of pain and rushing off into a pointless life, where all they had to do was get fat and be eaten without any possibility of having a little fun.

Perhaps I could watch horses being gelded, for they do not appear so ingenuous and helpless as do cows and bulls. But that affair with the bull calves was far too human to be tolerable.

It was Chuck who caught the calves, which he did with the utmost nonchalance. He rode slowly round the tramping, lowing and grazing beasts looking for his victims with a far-away expression on his face, and, having caught sight of what he wanted to see, he got the lasso clear and tried a throw. He was not wonderfully expert, not good enough for a circus. He could miss twice before he got the loop round the shaggy neck.

It was then that hands and heels came into action. He pulled and the frightened calf resisted and kicked out with its short thin legs; then Chuck rose in his stirrups and leaned back using the purchase of his heels—on which everything now depended. Chuck held on and as his horse backed, the poor little brute was dragged with it, drawn slowly towards its fate which awaited it in the form of the Professor's needle, Hobo's branding iron and Slattery's knife and the giant spatula.

Across the grass to where I sat ten yards away came the smell of the proceedings: the acrid stench of the burned hair on the haunch, where Hobo applied the branding iron with Lazy M's cattle mark, and then, after the cut, the smell of Slattery's ointment, a mixture of grease and hospital. It was brilliant how they got a rope round all four hooves, then pulled so that the calf fell on its side, where it lay staring, frightened and uncomprehending, at the world and man—four men who flung themselves upon that little hairy bundle with their instruments: syringe, red-hot iron, knives, scoops. Then it was released from its bonds and dashed off with a bellow of pain, all unwitting of its fate. And taciturn Chuck slowly rode off for the next victim.

It was not a thing you could watch for hours on end, and I soon went back to the camp and, instead, watched the women preparing a meal, opening tins, cleaning up and going quietly about their business.

We spent five days out there, and the lowing and trampling and smell of burned hair and ointment on Chuck and Slattery and the others, when they returned from their work in the gloaming, became our life. Each morning I rode out and watched Chuck throwing his lasso and listened to the bellows of the frightened, unsexed, little calves and was glad that no one had asked me to help. Then I went for long sweeps across the prairie, sometimes as far as some red cliffs six miles away, which had been the Apaches' last haunt, before they burned their final settler's farm and that brought all the cavalry down upon them and they fled south into Mexico. If I had ridden across those mountains, through the pass, spent the night by a stream and the next day crossed the ridge and gone down on the other side, it would have brought me to Skeleton Pass, where Geronimo finally surrendered to the soldiers and where the bus which brought me out west had stopped. I just rode a little way up and looked at the peaks and gave up the idea: the thought of our camp fire and the frying pan always stood between me and any lengthy expedition and adventure. But it did enable me to get that bit of Arizona tied up, that part of the world with its cacti and flinty bridle-tracks.

It was inevitable that a certain boredom descended upon all of us—except Slattery, of course. He was always on the point of bursting into a guffaw. He had taken a liking to me and considered me a funny man. The simplest occupations in which I might indulge always caused him to watch me with ill-restrained laughter, and he would turn to the others and say:

"Heavens—yes, that Swede, he's a one. . . ."

Yet when we were gathered round the fire in the evening there were traces of a serious side to Slattery. Occasionally he would get his face under control and talk about the future of cattle-ranching in the West, about prices, government subsidies, the irrigation plans for Lazy M and what could come out of them; and at such times he was as boring as anyone. Irrigation was his pet subject. He enjoyed Hassayamper's trust and favour because he didn't think the only solution for the ranch was to turn Lazy M into a tourist hotel as the professor and presumably Judah and certainly Mary Lou, the heiress, wished to do.

Mary Lou would have made a wonderful hostess with her loose-limbed sexiness, silver dollars clinking at her wrists, sombrero down over the root of her nose, taking her small tightrope-walker steps as she moved among the guests.

But Slattery believed in irrigation. There were no limits to what you could achieve with irrigation. The high air was there already. The dry pastures would become orchards and the gravel desert fields of wheat.

Yet even in such concrete plans there was always something, some aspect in which Slattery could see something funny, and that would set him off again and after a bit, having had his laugh out, he would have to stand up and straighten himself. It was beyond comprehension. He never told funny stories or joked with anyone. He seemed to be stuffed with a need to laugh.

For all his absurdity Slattery was almost the most entertaining of our companions, while we were out on the prairie. A sort of Boy Scout fever had come over the Professor in that environment; he wanted to show that there was more to him than the philosopher and the ladies' hairdresser. Hobo sang in the evenings and though he did change his repertoire, the songs were all on the one theme, and in the end we grew deaf to them. Mary Lou seemed deep in thought, perhaps about life itself, or about her former husband, or perhaps about Chisholm's suitability for doing the honours at Lazy M.

One morning, as I was about to start shaving outside our little tent, the Professor and Slattery came up to me. Slattery gazed at me in the evident expectation that I should do or say something funny, but the Professor, on the other hand, looked very serious. He thumped me on the chest with his knuckles and said:

"Don't shave till you've heard what I've got to say."

I was rather taken aback and Slattery's mounting hilarity did not make me feel any better.

"We're going to have a Helldorado at the end of the month," said the Professor. "We haven't of course spoken of it before. Well, I'm president of the Tombstone Chamber of Commerce and we have a Helldorado in the town here every year. We've been doing that for the last five years. We thought you might take a part this year. It's our big boom in the town. We get more than 10,000 tourists during the days we have it. Crystal Palace and every shop in the town lives half the year on the Helldorado. What do you say?"

I tried to think it out, while Slattery had his laugh.

"Helldorado," said I. "Isn't that a masquerade? No one's told me properly, and of course I've never asked."

"We live on the Helldorado. Besides it's darned good fun," explained the Professor. "It's like this. We turn the whole town back into what it was sixty, seventy years ago, when Hassayamper came here. Then we have performances three days running. We act old episodes from the town's history. On the first day, a few ordinary things: brawls in drinking dens, a little shooting on the streets. Everybody is dressed up in the things people wore in those days. On the second day we show some of the old mines, and people are allowed down into a number of shafts where the water hasn't penetrated yet. In the afternoon we do a hold-up of the diligence. The last day it's the Earp-Clanton fight."

"The fight in the OK corral?"

"That's it. We shoot like hell and pour ketchup over ourselves. People are crazy about it."

"Which others are in it? I'm not much of an actor. I've never done this sort of thing before."

"The whole town's in it. Every single person. In the evenings the college girls dance the can-can in Crystal Palace, and Mary Lou presides at the bar, and my wife takes part and my daughter. . . . Everyone in the town is in it and does something. Titus too. He's usually a cardsharper or something like that."

77

"And what would I be?"

"You can think about that. You could be one of the Clanton boys who are shot by Earp and his brothers. I don't think you've got enough experience to be one of Earp's brothers. We'll think out something. Margareta can be a siren in Crystal Palace. We have masses of pretty dresses she can try."

It sounded amusing and I said so, at the same time dipping my shaving-brush into the mug of hot water which I had just got from Hobo.

"But you must stop shaving," said the Professor laying his hand on my arm. "Whatever you're going to be, you must have a moustache, and if you're to be one of the Clanton boys, you'll need a half-beard and have the rest unshaven. If you could ever get a gallop out of Eve, you could also help hold up the diligence."

They walked off towards their horses to ride out to the branding. Slattery laughed so that he shook as he walked, and as he passed Mary Lou and Hobo at the cook's waggon he jerked his thumb in my direction:

"What did I tell you? The Swede'll do it. He'll be the best blackguard they've had in Tombstone."

I crawled into our tent where Margareta was beginning to wake up, and started to dress.

"Grown tired of shaving?" asked Margareta.

"I'm to be a blackguard in the Tombstone pageant. You're a harlot in Crystal Palace. We're to be in the Helldorado, which seems to be something like the Oberammergau Passion Play only with the OK corral in place of Golgotha. Everybody has his definite part, and presumably it's a great honour to be invited to take part. Maybe they are badly off for scoundrels and prostitutes."

All that morning I spent hidden behind the cook's waggon trying my sombrero in various positions, beetling my brows and sneering scornfully in an attempt to make myself look blackguardly. I was quite excited at the thought of being able to play at Wild West in earnest: a game it was, of course, but still as serious as it could be, for would I not be helping Tombstone to attract tourists and do business? After a substantial lunch alone with the girls I rode off on Eve to train for the attack on the diligence.

That day I went and watched the calves being branded from a little closer than ten yards. I thought that I ought to start accustoming myself to the spectacle, if I was to represent a cowboy, whether a blackguardly one or honest. On the way back to the camp I had a further talk with the Professor and learned that this was an extra Helldorado; the ordinary one was held in the autumn, but the *Epitaph* was celebrating its seventy-fifth anniversary that spring and they felt it would do no harm to beat the big drum a bit.

Not till we sat having dinner did I notice that all the men were unshaven. We were preparing for our Passion Play. You could see no difference in Chuck. He always had a ring of down round his chin from ear to ear and a tendency to whiskers. Hobo too was perpetually unshaven. But the professor-cum-ladies' hairdresser was something of a sensation. He had the pink and cherished complexion of the super-healthy American, and though he normally wore a beard, the least hint of unkemptness beyond its limits immediately caught your eye. He had begun to look rather lousy and unreliable.

"What's your part, Professor?" I asked.

"A sheriff who takes bribes," he answered with the utmost calm.

Hobo was to be a scoundrelly, drunken miner and gold-digger, which Slattery said did not call for any acting on his part, and Slattery himself was to play the chief blackguard, Ike Clanton. He seemed to be wrongly cast, for his description of him was that of a glum and melancholy murderer, and I could not see how Slattery was going to work the transformation.

That afternoon and evening Mary Lou was like a girl in her teens, immersed in confidential giggling whisperings with Margareta and Ysabel about how they were to dress. Margareta was to be one of the hostesses in Crystal Palace, and Ysabel was to make her debut on the stage in the can-can.

It was all very silly and naive, but welcome, for life out on the prairie had grown tedious and the plans lent life and colour to the days.

Otherwise we longed to be back at Hassayamper's fireside.

The last evening we sat in tired silence watching the fire die down. We washed our gullets with fizzy drinks after a heavy meal, and the night was cool and dark-blue, surfeited and full of repose. Slowly I came to realize that we had been away out in the wilds, that at home I could scarcely have got farther from civilization by going to Lapland—well, perhaps yes, but those were wilds so popular and written about that everyone tritely expressed a longing to go there, while man in his heart had really abandoned the arid plain we were on.

Slattery dreamed of making it fertile with irrigation channels. Perhaps Chuck, who had once had to shoot the horse that had carried him across it, also dreamed of it, though in a different way. For though he really was a plumber, he did not look at the prairie with any thought of irrigation, nor measure it for pipes with his mind's eye. He rode off each evening, and no one asked whither he rode, and none knew where he had been when he returned. He could come riding across the rise in the morning as we were turning out for breakfast, with a night spent God knows how in the wilds behind him.

Sometimes Margareta and I used to whisper about him in our tent, and I told her the little I knew, that he had a wife who was never seen and that he was always riding outside Tombstone, along the asphalt road in the moonlight or in the pitch darkness among the rocks. That he repaired whatever broke or went wrong, and that he sat late in Crystal Palace without taking too much, yet with a more and more bizarre expression about his eyes for every glass he took. He never seemed to be in a hurry, and yet it was he who did everything in those parts: installed bathrooms and W.Cs and repaired the Professor's Fords and put in bookcases and greased the old diligence which Judah kept in a barn for the Helldorado, and he was head of the fire brigade, read books which he got from the Professor's lending library. . . .

We asked Slattery in one of his rare moments of irrigational seriousness about him and he said:

"Chuck is placid. He knows the prairie and is good friends with every day."

We sat silent listening to that as though the words were echoing, then Slattery went on:

"He is the industrious friend of the dawn. He keeps holiday in the forenoon. He is very intimate with the day as the hours come along. In the middle of the day, which is so hard for us others, he is wideawake and lively; and he is the confidant of night."

Those were the last words of value spoken out on the prairie.

The next day we packed up our things, knives, brushes, syringes and empty bottles and rode back to Lazy M.

It was by the old schoolhouse with its dream of the check-shirted schoolmistress that I suddenly became filled with a longing for glistening, wet streets, blazing lights and listless bars with wan, washed-out girls, bridges across water with barges, and wind blowing round dismal street corners. I imagine that I must have had enough of lofty solitude in the wilds and of that field of vision which was filled by sky and a plain in which the hundreds of cattle and some few humans were scarcely visible protuberances. Time after time, with the blue evening sky enfolding us and the horses stepping high-leggedly along, my longing conjured up the vision of a blustery street corner, of neon lights with their warm promises on the fronts of desolate buildings.

I wished I were in a big city.

I wondered if the wilds can have any natural attraction for man, whether all we say about their beauty is not just so much talk, said because we think we ought to like such things.

As a child you did not like natural beauty. If there was a whole forest in front of you and you found a forgotten builder's hod, or there was a tumbledown shed on the fringe of the wood, it was with the hod or the shed that you played. It was only much later, when you were grown up and spoilt and the lying myths of the mushroom seeker and the idealisms of the hiker had laid hold of you, that you got it into your head that what you were really longing for was nature.

I realized even while I took mental flight from the prairie, that with me it was not as Slattery had said of Chuck: I was not good friends with the day, I was not the wideawake confidant of the noonday hour; I had slipped my moorings and slid away from what was close to me.

I rode up level with Margareta:

"It's rather ridiculous," I said, "but I have an awful longing to be back in Chicago."

10

THE SPIRIT OF A CITY

Nostalgically I thought of one cold December afternoon in Ashland Avenue, when the wind came howling obliquely off Lake Michigan past the engineering workshops and the electricians' shops and the Polish butchers' shops that were like empty caves, and you felt that the entire populace had died out and the world was empty. The pavements were built-up, a thing I could never understand in Chicago, and so you had to climb at every street corner when you crossed. Many of the stone flags were broken. At times the wind shut its eyes to everything but a garbage bin and concentrated on that, as if it had sworn by all the boreal gods that it was going to have that over. And so it would in the end. The bin hung on as long as it could beside the door where the negro porter had put it, then it began slowly sliding along the pavement, scraping on the stone, till it bumped into some unevenness, wobbled and fell; then with a whoop of triumph the wind swept off and away up the avenue with greasy wrappings, newspaper and old tins.

Where there were no workshops, there were dwelling-houses with paper replacing broken window-panes and steps down to the street, as often as not lacking a hand-rail, that having fallen off. All life was on the other side, at the back, where there were wooden verandas along every storey on which washing was hung out and children sat on stools eating hunky sandwiches with toy revolvers lying beside them, and, below, men with the day off washed their cars beside heaps of refuse.

I do not remember what had taken me to town that day. It was just before Christmas and I was living in a villa out at Evanston, where Michigan is like a heavy, fresh sea. I could have walked out along the friendly piers of the yacht harbour or strolled along the beach roads between the houses and the lake, yet after a breakfast of coffee at a drug store, I had drifted down to the station and taken a train in to town. I had not even gone as far as the Loop, but had got off up there among the dead house-walls and shut workshops and smashed window-panes.

Late in the forenoon, in the midst of all that desolation, I went to a place for a cup of coffee, for I was not feeling like lunch. It was a self-service restaurant with tiled walls and tiled floor and tiled ceiling, like a swimming-bath or a public lavatory. You went in; there were benches and chairs and tables, but no friendliness; behind the counter stood a pretty, slatternly girl with a sailor's hat pulled low over her forehead; she leaned apathetically towards the customers and passed on their orders to the kitchen behind her:

"Chicken soup. Chicken soup."

The words echoed like in a swimming-bath.

I took my place in the queue behind an old man who was reading a newspaper called *Der Illinois Tag*, using both spectacles and a magnifying glass. He held the paper close up to his eyes. The seams were burst in his jacket, and I could see that he had some sort of summer jacket on underneath. He wore a peculiar black hat that looked quite out of place in those American surroundings.

He took his tray and had a lengthy conference with the girl who called out "Chicken soup" about what he should eat, but though he hesitated a long time, he ended up with just a slice of rye bread and a cup of coffee, and with this on his tray he carefully made his way to a table at which sat another man in black, threadbare clothes:

"*Na, Alois, wie geht's dir,*" he said, and they relapsed into muttered converse about things very far from Ashland Avenue. I eavesdropped and realized that they were from Bohemia.

Every five minutes a tram thundered past outside. Over the way was an empty plot with the carcass of an old car lying in it and the fence of a parking place for its background. In the building facing us was a strip-tease bar looking desolate and chill in the pale midday sunlight. Outside it hung a photomontage life-size picture of a girl in a state of undress; the wind was making her grey-white charms billow out and someone made a joke about it over his cup of coffee. The two Bohemians were even deeper in converse. The smaller one, wearing the two jackets, seemed able to make his slice of bread and cup of coffee last for ever. Moving his hands in a sort of slow-motion he produced a spectacle case and folded his spectacles away in it. I am sure at least two trams passed before he had restored the case to its place and buttoned up his top jacket again. Then he leaned forward and resumed his talk with Alois. They were far away in their beloved Bohemia. Even their hats were strangely un-American, despite their having been bought in a cheap clothing store in the Loop; perhaps it was because they were on heads that could never be part of the New World. The girl kept calling out "Chicken soup. Chicken soup," and the wind was getting up. Poles in peaked caps walked past, head down to the blast. They must have had those caps with them when they came to Chicago, or perhaps some enterprising Pole manufactured caps on the old model and sold them. They struggled against the wind with their hands in their pockets and shouted things to their wives, who followed them with bags filled with potatoes and corn and vegetables.

I sat on listlessly and had no one to talk to, as the Bohemians had. Then I went and walked for several blocks in the wind, but came back and asked for another cup of coffee. I was almost alone there now. Suddenly, on the other side of the street I saw an old man in threadbare clothes. He was cautiously crawling along the wall of the houses close by the still unopened strip-tease bar, holding both hands pitifully extended to maintain the balance of his hollow body. When he reached the edge of the pavement, he shrank from taking the steep step down, and as he stood there hesitating, he suddenly fell flat on his back and remained there inert. That was between North Clark and Rush. Something crunched as he fell. It was a flat flask he had had in his hip pocket, but he hit his head on the stone at the same time.

I ran out on to the street, then went back in again and told the girl who called "Chicken soup" to telephone for an ambulance, and when I got to the old man there were already several people standing round him: a tall, fat man with a bedraggled cigar in his mouth, an old Pole in a peaked cap, and a girl who must have been going to the bar, for she was wearing a fur coat and a dress that somehow was open to her belly and let you glimpse some skin and a ribbon that presumably was part of her bust-bodice: everything hung loose on her: furs, flesh and clothes.

The Pole and I raised the old man to his feet, for he said that there was nothing wrong with him and asked to be lifted up. Once he was on his feet, his trousers suddenly came down with a run. It was all the more peculiar, as they had stuck up all right when he came crawling along the street just a moment before. It was as though they had been jerked down with a string. There we stood on a street corner in Chicago in the icy blast, four of us round a trembling old man displaying a lot of white and shrivelled skin, while trams thundered past and three million people hurried on their various ways through the asphalt landscape. We stood there, timid and hesitant, with the old man's nakedness between us, then the fat one with the cigar bent down and pulled the trousers up over the old man's blue, shivering legs. Then the ambulance came and we helped him in; I let go of his arm and left the hygienic, white-garbed ambulance man to see to him, and when I turned away the little crowd had already dispersed. The fat man was waddling towards a doorway, the old Pole was some distance up the street telling the tale in Polish to a huddle of his fellows, and the girl was clattering on high heels towards the bar.

The endlessness of North Clark, then down Ashland again—I do not know how many times I walked down Ashland Avenue in the wind that day, past the workshops and the empty windows. When I saw the lights from the Loop, it was like an island, a sanctuary awaiting me with peace and reconciliation. I went to Schlogl's. There was a large stag's head hanging from the ceiling, and it was dark and gloomy and everyone seemed to know everyone else and be whispering together; it was as though there were a conspiracy of jest and confidences, and I was the only one who was not initiated. I ordered goulash and thought it revolting with its small pieces of meat and bits of fat, till I remembered that it had been exactly the same on the previous occasion I had been there. But then I had been a tourist and literary pilgrim, and a wizened old boy from the *Chicago Daily News* had pointed out where Sandburg and Sherwood Anderson and Ben Hecht used to sit in 1916. Now, I had come merely to eat, out of sheer absent-mindedness, as I fumbled with a day for which I really had no use.

I turned northwards again, crossed the river and walked down the passage to Silver Frolics, which was one of the more elegant strip-tease bars. I had never been there, for it was where all the tourists went and I was doubtful of its genuineness, but it was almost Christmas and I felt that I could give myself a treat. Usually there was a porter either outside or just inside the door, but he was gone and I walked into an atmosphere almost like that of a private house or of a night-club two storeys up in Berlin, and it made me feel uncomfortable. A bar should be a bar and no nonsense about it. Just as I had told myself that I did not like the upholstery and draperies and mirrors, and had decided not to stay, a solemn little group swept past me as in a dream: two men conducting a third to the door. Their faces and movements were grave and solemn, and it was difficult to realize that the one in the middle was being led away against his will. He held his head high and though he was being forced along, his gait was in no way constrained. A smile played about his lips. The other two looked very determined, but even when having to exert force they maintained their dignity.

Suddenly, I realized that I knew the man they were chucking out, so, as the waiter and porter disappeared with him down the stairs I had just come up, I turned and followed.

It was Frank they had chucked out. He was editor of a local paper that was published twice weekly in a nice residential district to the north of Chicago. He had been at Iwo Jima and had been decorated for gallantry, and he had a tiny little fiancée who only came up to his waist. He was always very calm and cheerful. I did not know him intimately, but when I saw him being marched out I remembered that it was Friday, and that on another Friday about a month before, I had been in his office and heard him say:

"Hell, let's go into town and set some money circulating."

This, apparently, was a pet expression of his which had acquired local notoriety, for he always celebrated pay day.

When I reached the foot of the steps from Silver Frolics Frank was standing fairly steadily on the pavement, smiling to himself and repeating:

"Well, well. Well, I never."

I went up to him and he was delighted to have company, but nothing was ever said of why he had been chucked out of Silver Frolics. He had a car parked in Rush Street in the shadow of the skyscrapers of Michigan Avenue. The great avenue spanned that landscape of corrugated iron and excrement and dilapidated wooden houses like a footbridge. When you were an outcast at the corner of Rush and North Clark it glowed festively like a Jacob's ladder and the gleam of it plunged deep into your consciousness; it was a rebuff that made you realize that you were

86

sorry and down, that the day had besmirched you with dust and dirt from the strap-handles of trams and grease from the dirty table-tops of cheap café bars, and that you were not made for Sherarton's lounge and bar, but must stay where you were, down in the slough under the bridge.

Thus Frank and I set off into the labyrinth of the shanty-town.

As Frank was not sober I thought I had better drive and got into the driver's seat. His old Oldsmobile was wedged in pretty tightly, and Frank thought I was being far too meek and mild over trying to extricate it, so he pushed me aside and took over. He revved up the engine and began a pendulum movement, savagely backing and bounding forward. For three minutes he was like a madman, banging at the car in front of him and jabbing at the one behind; there was a great deal of rattle and clatter, and the line of parked cars was set swaying the whole length of the block. Then with a triumphant blare of his horn Frank swung out into the carriageway and made way for me at the wheel.

We drove first to the bars in North Clark. In the first we sat at a bar that went in serpentine bends to link up with itself. Inside it was a stage on which girls appeared and danced. They wore queer veils that were neither clothes nor even pieces of material, just thin scales that they peeled off their bodies. I perched on an empty stool and after a while a girl with mother-of-pearl spectacles and long yellow hair and frowning forehead came and scolded the bartender for letting me sit there, and kept on about it even though I moved at once. The bartender flung out his arms and muttered: "Jesus Christ, Jesus Christ."

The girl who was dancing and stripping herself had a long and really lovely back. All that went on in front: her loose expression and routine obscene gestures were ugly; but her back was white like a temple and beautiful, and I decided that I would look at that so as not to feel ashamed. That back was made for a lover on a bathing beach or in bed on a Sunday morning when she could yawn and roll over, and it had no business to be where it was. Why had she dragged it there? It should never have been taken among bottles reflecting artificial light, the heavy longing looks from half-tight insurance agents and estate agents, or the deadly avid eyes behind mother-of-pearl mounted rims beneath a wrinkled brow; it was a lovely back, horribly defiled. Girls' backs have two small dips, like bowls, on either side of the small of the back.

87

We said, "What the hell, let's get out of here," but as so often happens when you say that and act on it, you only find yourself in another place exactly similar. We were now lower down North Clark, and the only difference was that the girls danced up on the bar. In between turns a boy appeared and told homosexual jokes, and the girls changed quickly and came to the bar and put one arm under your jacket from behind and asked for a drink.

Still jaunty, we said "What the hell, let's get out of this," and five minutes later we were in a bar on West Madison called Music Box, and there you had to walk through the bar itself, and we sat at a table close up to the stage on which stood a woman compere reeling off homosexual jokes. She was big and heavy with thin legs, and her charms were heavy lowering clouds over light-coloured birches, but where we sat we saw no more than her worn shoes and the threadbare toes of her stockinged feet. A girl danced and smilingly pretended to squirt us from her breast, and then she came and took us by the knee. We went to the next bar which had a French name, Chez something. There there was a dusty, pasty-faced, cavernous girl who put one hand behind her on the floor and, thus straddled, walked squirming to the bar with a thin black cord no broader than a pleat between her legs, and another girl who had tattooing on her left thigh and who afterwards came and told us she was Turkish. Whether that was a joke or a slang expression, I do not know, but then she drew her breast out from her dress and pinched and pulled at the nipple as though it had been made of rubber and said that we could do the same for a dollar, but we did not think it worth the money.

We got into Frank's car and tore down Ashland through the cold grey night, through the area of the slaughter-houses, past dust bins and empty plots. At times, if we got too far out into the street, the car skidded on the wet tramway lines. When we drove across Chicago University campus, it was like switching off the visions of our night, and for a brief minute we enjoyed a heavenly dream of green lawns and Virginia creeper and belfries. We were soon through it however, and in following Frank's confused directions I got ourselves lost on South Side. We drove under the railway, along which the early trains with workers for the slaughter-houses thundered in the faint early light. We went into bars, taking into each a little of the December haze from out-side, like a thin veil of ice that settled on the negroes when they

88

caught sight of us. I looked at the negresses' long stick-like arms and legs with dangling ornaments and thin gold chains round their ankles. I felt how immeasurably stupid we were coming in with forced expressions on our faces, playing at being intelligent whites who did not mind being on South Side, and who were quite prepared to say something friendly and encouraging to the coloured people we met in the night. A negress dancer in one bar was lewder than all the white girls in Clark and Madison, yet she still retained a certain grace, a thought that I had not even thought to the end, before it tasted vapid and semi-literary.

I grew more and more unamused by the night, and in the end made Frank turn west and north at every corner, which gave the general direction of our residential township. We got to Dearborn Station and found a place next to a garage where we could have coffee. It was morning and the typists were already on their way to their offices and the charwomen in the Polish kerchiefs to their homes; Frank told me that the *Tribune*, Chicago's biggest newspaper, was conducting a campaign against those kerchiefs as un-American, and it was quite right. The Poles would never become Americans so long as they stuck to their kerchiefs and peaked caps, he said.

Having drunk my coffee, it occurred to me that I had not eaten anything for a very long time, that I would have to go to a bank and that a new day had begun. Gradually I began to pull myself together. This new day was greyer and rawer than the one I had just been through, yet in some queer way I felt kindly towards it; it was a day I could be friends with, and that was why I had suddenly remembered it all as I rode back to Lazy M with Margareta. Slattery had said that Chuck was a friend of the day. I had the whole time been at loggerheads with the days we had spent out with the cattle and in our camp, and that is why I had remembered that morning in the city, when I had neither slept nor eaten, and had been greasy and unkempt and yet had managed to get along with the hours. I went first to Sherarton Hotel and had a bath and a shave and bought a new shirt. Then I drifted through the hall and out on to the street and had bacon and eggs on Michigan Avenue and wrote a long letter. I went to the Art Museum and had a look at Modigliani, but I spent even longer on the small miniature models of colonial furniture which a lady with white hair had made in her spare time. As I walked up

Randolph Street I saw on a door plate that Chicago's electricians' Trade Union had its offices there, and I went in and talked with a Swede about sickness benefit and piece-work and gangsters; gangsters were always trying to get into the Trade Unions and get hold of their bank accounts, he said. I bought some cigars and went out to the Technical Museum and looked at aged aeroplanes hanging from the roof and at myself in television. I went over a slaughter-house, and the stench of marrow-bones and hides stabbed through me like a headache. The corn exchange was swarming with dealers making lightning signs at each other, or walking gravely to the bags of wheat and soya beans that stood on tables at one end of the room, or looking at the weather reports from Dakota and Manitoba and thinking of winds and the rain that might come from Medicine Hat. In the huge halls of the skyscrapers in the Loop, cigar butts showered down into the concrete tubs filled with sand that stood outside the lifts.

In the afternoon I went to the Swedish America Line's offices on Michigan Avenue and sat on a sofa by the window pretending to be interested in sending gift parcels. An old man who had no overcoat, but just a jacket and narrow trousers and used a stick, fished with trembling fingers in a notecase to produce a Swedish identity certificate and his money, chuckling all the while. He was going back to Sweden which he had left in 1904, and he wondered if anyone there would recognize him. The man who sold him his ticket said that he did not know, but he expected somebody would.

That evening, when I had been in Chicago for twenty-seven hours without sleeping, I found myself standing where Michigan Avenue is thrown up like a bastion before dropping down to the fire station that delighted Oscar Wilde so and to the smart clubs in Gothe Street and to the millionaires' palaces in prairie Gothic on the beach promenade. I looked out across the landscape lying beneath the bastion: the neon lights were being lit on the bars in Rush Street and the chucker-out was taking up his station outside Silver Frolics. The circle was complete. Far away in Ashland Avenue another garbage tin would be blowing over, but I had got myself safely up on to the bridge that spanned the slough.

And then, at last, I took the train back to where I had a room in a house with a lawn.

11

WYATT AND THE DOC

Lazy M had been a place of gloom while we were away. Hassayamper had been talking business with Titus, who had lots of money, a fact that irritated the old chap, and the Apache queen had not made things any more cheerful. However, with a crowd round him and many ears waiting to hear his stories Hassayamper recovered his spirits, and on the very evening of our return—it was a hot, still evening, yet we lit the fire just the same—he told us about Boot Hill.

Gradually things became more cheeful. Not that Titus had ever been sulky—no matter how many suggestions he had made, nor how angry Hassayamper had become because he saw that one day he would have to accept one of these suggestions and let the little hump-backed fruit-farmer have a share in the ranch as well. There was always a self-assurance about both Titus' movements and his expression that set him a little above others. He had nothing to worry about. He had money, money that was safe, for it grew in Californian soil. Nor could things happen to him as they might to us others, for he was already broken and bowed: neither illness nor an accident could spoil things for him, and that was why, for all his wretchedness, he seemed to be unusually invulnerable, calmly leaning on the Indian gods of destiny, in sublime acceptance of all life's vicissitudes. He liked being close to the fire.

We had had a good dinner and now some cognac, remarkable un-American cognac such as you would scarcely get after a dinner in New York; then Hassayamper with a slight smile and an apologetic gesture in the direction of Margareta and me—apparently we were supposed to be the most inquisitive—began his tale.

"I can never remember Earp coming to Tombstone," said Hassayamper. "Two of his brothers came at the same time as my father. But there was nothing funny in that. There was a rush to the town then. Father had heard about the place and the mines and how all South Arizona was full of silver. He had heard it in bars up in Abilene and on the Western Trail—but however it was, my mother also believed it and so they set off, father with his money sewn into his belt. I don't believe he ever seriously intended to dig for gold and silver. He came here to do business, and he probably had cattle in mind too, for that was what he knew about. To start with he opened a shop and sold clothes to the miners, special clothes to wear down in the galleries of the mines. He made a lot out of that. Then some years later he began buying grazing land and built Lazy M.

"I don't remember anything of our coming to Tombstone, and I wouldn't be certain now of the date, if I hadn't come across some old bills and papers of my father's. We came here in the spring of 1879. I had two sisters in those days, Annabelle and Sue Ellen, both grown-up.

"The town looked roughly as it does now, except that close on ten thousand people lived in it. Beyond the last houses were tents and waggons in which the miners lived with their families. Otherwise there weren't any more houses than today. What usually happened was that people like us, families and such come to work for others or to set up a business, either lived in tents or, if they could, found accommodation in the attics of some house in the town. The bachelors, the gold-diggers who were really making money, the owners of real estate, the bartenders, editor Clum of the *Epitaph*, the Earp boys, the loose women—such folk always lived in one or other of the hotels. There was Cosmopolitan, Alhambra, Occidental and a couple more. They had proper carpets on the floors and menus printed in French. We went to one for lunch every Sunday, after church. They were just building the episcopal church when we came, the same as is there today, and I remember that until it was finished the Rev. Roberts, he was an Englishman and had been at Oxford and come out here to collect flowers, used to preach among the scaffolding, even when the church was still just a few planks. To raise the money to build it, we got up a dance after service every Sunday. That is my first real memory of Tombstone, so the town can't have been only bloody and tough. The families used to come out to the church site and sing psalms, and afterwards a band would play square dances and then we all went and had lunch at the fine hotels. As often as not we had no more than a hundred yards to walk, yet those Sundays were like being in a different town, and it would be evening before we got home.

"We lived and had our shop opposite the fire-station. Obliquely across the way was OK corral, and the *Epitaph* was in the house next to ours. The *Epitaph* is about the only thing in the town that has moved since then—the paper and I. There were the same streets then as now. From north to south First up to and including Seventh Street, and from west to east Toughnut, Allen and Fremont. There aren't any more now, nor were there then. I believe Tombstone was a bit different from other towns in the West in that its houses had such narrow gable-ends to the street. Then they extended back to the courtyards behind like long guts. The houses in Tombstone have always been damned long and narrow.

"We lived in Fremont between Third and Fourth, and St. Paul's episcopal church was in Third, just as it is now; Crystal Palace at the corner of Allen and Fifth—you hear, all just as now, nothing's changed. Only there was a heck of a lot more saloons and bars and hotels in those days. Up at the corner of Fifth and Toughnut—what is there now? Oh yes, some Mexican has a piddling little workshop there—was the town's finest brothel, if you'll pardon the word, Nellie's. They had an 'erotic circus' every Thursday evening. I was too small to go and see it, and by the time I was old enough, the brothel no longer functioned; but I remember what it was like inside, for when I was a kid I was often sent there on errands. If you hung about outside, somebody would always open a window and ask you to run and buy him some shaving soap, or fetch his pistols, or go for his horse, or something, and you always got a dollar for your pains.

"Toughnut isn't much to look at these days, but it was all along there that the miners lived. These were either fools who prospected in the mountains on their own account, or those who worked in the galleries or at the pumps and lifts. They were well paid, but they were crazy gamblers and money just ran through their fingers, however much they earned. It was pitiful to see their poor wives standing waiting outside the gambling saloons in the evenings, hoping their husbands might slip them a coin or two for the children, but I don't believe they ever did. Not many in any case. There was a gaming saloon at every corner and several billiard rooms and bowling halls. And everywhere you had to bet. If a town lives on miners and crazy fools searching for silver and gold, and a horde of shopkeepers live on the fools, and

93

there are gaming saloons and whores galore—then usually the devil gets loose and no mistake. People sort of feel that they have to be tough with each other. When people play cards or faro someone has to lose, and whoever lost then became a vicious savage with two revolvers strung round him. If he still had money, he could afford to treat a girl and that would make him happy, but then they would fall out, or something would go wrong, and he would be as nasty as ever. Wherever you turned, there were always angry men armed with a couple of revolvers.

"Getting shot was the simplest thing in the world in those days. There were two decent old miners called Waters and Bradshaw. They had lived together in all sorts of mining camps before they came to Tombstone. They were both prospectors, but as they had had no luck for a long time, they were working in the Convention Mine. One Saturday afternoon Waters had been to my father's shop and bought a check shirt, black and blue with red outlines. There was nothing really remarkable about it, unless perhaps the checks were a little louder than such shirts usually are. However that may be, several good friends whom Waters met said to him:

" 'That's a damned smart shirt.'

"On Saturdays Waters always went the rounds, having a few drinks, looking in at Nellie Cashman's brothel and playing a game or two of bowls—quiet, little bachelor amusements of no great pretentions. On this particular Saturday he drank enough for him to get quite angry with all the remarks people were passing about his shirt. About six o'clock he walked into Crystal Palace. The bartender served him the whisky and water he ordered, and then remarked that it was a darned smart shirt he was wearing.

"Waters seized the bartender by his tie and shirt front and pulled him half across the bar. People rushed up wondering what was happening, but Waters just held the barman there with the poor chap's nose close to the zinc, and said to him:

" 'Now I'm tired and fed up with all you people who don't like my shirt. If I meet another who finds my shirt's not to his taste, I'll put a bullet into him and no argument. If anyone has any remarks to make about my shirt let him come forward now, for after this I'm just going to shoot.'

"Waters was a big hefty man and usually most good-natured, but they all realized that he was really angry now and that the safest thing was to forget his shirt. The bartender said that he had meant no offence, that, in fact, he liked the shirt very much.

" 'Shut your mouth,' said Waters.

"For the next half hour he just sat in silence, glowering; then he got up and announced that he was going across to Corrigan's bowling saloon to see if there might not be some damned son of a bitch there, who would find the shirt not to his taste. It almost sounded as though he were angry that no one had come and quarrelled with him about it.

"In the very doorway of Crystal Palace he met his friend Bradshaw. Bradshaw was ten years older than Waters and a small, insignificant chap who always went about trembling slightly at the thought of all the gold that he never found. He was not a talkative being, but when he met his chum in the doorway his face lit up and he said:

" 'Have you seen the like of that! There's a fancy shirt for you!'

"Waters hit him between the eyes, and Bradshaw dropped like a pole-axed bullock.

"Then Waters disappeared on his round of the bars, trying to start a quarrel about his shirt, but by this time most people had heard that he was looking for trouble and were warned.

"Bradshaw was helped to his feet and into Crystal Palace and after a while he recovered. He went behind the bar and washed the blood off his face. He did not say a word and people were a bit anxious lest the blow had knocked him funny. He had a couple of drams at the bar, but if anyone asked what had happened, or tried to cheer him up, he just shook his head; and then he disappeared.

"Some hours later, when darkness had fallen, someone happened to notice that old Bradshaw was sitting balancing on a chair outside Crystal Palace. He had been home and changed and was in his Sunday best. He sat with the chair tilted against the house-wall and his feet on an old whisky cask standing on the wooden foot-walk. His expression was a bit odd, and he held one hand rather queerly under his jacket, but no one thought there was anything dangerous about him, merely that he was feeling mortified or perhaps had a pain somewhere, and so people spoke to him and commiserated with him, and he just nodded and never said a word.

"All at once Waters came walking along, still in his shirt. He was in better humour now, for he had been in Nellie's brothel where a man had seen the shirt on a nail and said something about it, and Waters had flown straight at him and flung him into a big mirror. He was now intending to have a good-night beer in Crystal Palace and then go home to bed. As he stepped up on to the footwalk, old Bradshaw rose to his feet. Waters saw him and waved cheerfully to him, thinking that his having hit him would have been forgotten and forgiven. But Bradshaw just gazed at him gravely and said:

" 'You should never have done that, Waters.'

"Then he pulled out a revolver that he had kept hidden under his jacket, and fired four shots into his old friend, all into the heart.

"I'm telling you this, and I was there and heard the shots and saw them carry Waters away, so that you can see that in those days it was enough to be wearing a new shirt to get yourself shot in Tombstone.

"Sometime in the summer of 1879 my father took in a very strange lodger. He was given an old store-room that was no longer used and which my mother smartened up nicely with flowered curtains and a large washhand stand and a portrait of President Grant. He was a small, pale-faced chap with large drooping black moustaches and was known as the Doctor, which was shortened to Doc. Doc Holliday. He had been a dentist, and it was always said that he had come West for the sake of his lungs. He may very well have done so for sometimes in his room at night and in the mornings, he coughed most dreadfully. But it was also known, at least to my father, that the Doc had shot a negro in Georgia, where his home was. He had gone to a lake in which he and some other white boys used to swim, intending to have a bathe, and when he saw a negro bathing on the other side, he rowed across and shot him. He was of course drunk. Nobody locally was horrified at what he had done, but his father thought it uncomfortable having him at home—a son who went about shooting people like that, so he sent him away. Before that the Doc had been attending some dental college or other, so he went back there and got his diploma, but I wonder if he ever practised. At any rate it was impossible to get him to help anyone with toothache in Tombstone. He always found some excuse to get out of doing anything.

"Doc Holliday was a gambler. It was a madness with him. He had come West with a little of his father's money in his pocket, and this he gambled and lost. He managed to buy and sell some horses and made a bit that way, and so he began gambling again, systematically. He rode all round the West or went by diligence from town to town and from camp to camp and sat himself down at the poker tables. He looked insignificant and pitiable with his chalky face above big black moustaches, and he was always having to produce his handkerchief and cough, and when he coughed it was like an aged railway engine going up a steep rise; you could scarcely believe such a little fellow could produce such noises.

"He would sit as long as you liked at a poker game or faro table and never turn a hair. All day and night if need be. I saw him countless times in Tombstone, hat down over his eyes, big raven-black eyes glued to the cards, and then his giant moustache. He inspired tremendous respect, even when he was really just a boy. When he came to Tombstone he could not have been more than twenty-four, twenty-five, yet all the old poker foxes looked up to him with deference. Card-sharpers knew that it was not worth starting anything with him, or trying to diddle him. He could shoot.

"He had realized that he must be able to shoot, so he had spent all his free time practising. In the mornings he sat and shot at things from his hotel window, he shot from the diligence when he was travelling, and all who tried to stop him were told to go to hell. Unlike Earp he really had killed people—not just that nigger at the lake, but a couple of fellows who had made a nuisance of themselves at the poker table. He killed people without turning a hair. It was nothing to him. You could see that by his eyes. He was utterly cold. If you happened to be standing beside him at a bar and saw into his eyes for a moment or two, it was like looking close at a corpse. People were just dirt to him. He plugged them when it pleased him, and that was all there was about it.

"I remember what excitement there was the afternoon father told us that he had met Doc Holliday in Crystal Palace. The Doc had asked where he might get a room, and my father had said that he had one empty. We all helped to make it neat and trim, dusting and scrubbing, all very busy. We all knew who the Doc was; you could not live in the West without hearing about all its personalities. But there was something sinister about Doc Holliday's reputation—Earp, you knew, was an honest chap, calm and safe and always on the side of the law. But the Doc was a gambler and a murderer—his reputation was a bogey that went ahead of him warning people to keep quiet. As my sisters and I were on our knees scrubbing, we thought how the murderer was on his way to our house and was going to live there. At the same time we were not so greatly terrified, for we knew that he did not shoot people just for the fun of it: you had to be sitting playing cards with him and try to cheat him, if you were to be shot, and that was not a thing that really offended anyone. Naturally we admired him—presumably my father did so too. People were like that in the West in the old days. And they stayed like it.

"We seldom saw the Doc while he was living with us. He got up late and took a long time dressing. The arrangement was that he should have coffee and a slice of bread in the morning, and this mother put down for him outside his door and he took it in when no one was looking. He must have been shy. At about two in the afternoon he eventually emerged into the light of day and then he always saluted politely if he met one of us, but he never said anything. He walked across to the Occidental which had the smartest dining room in those days, and there he had lunch and read a paper, and when that was finished he used to settle in a corner and play patience or do card tricks for himself, and after that he went to Crystal Palace or wherever he had decided to play that evening. He would come home some time during the night, if anything more quietly than when he left in the morning.

"I never understood, nor did anyone else for that matter, how Wyatt Earp and the Doc could be such good friends. The bond must have been gambling. Earp was always on the side of the law. The Doc was always suspected of any attack made on a diligence anywhere near where he was. He was never arrested or convicted, but there were plenty of diligence drivers and shot-guns who would swear that it was the Doc who had robbed them. Earp even suffered because of his friendship with the Doc. He was himself suspected of being up to tricks. But he just shook his head and went out and had a meal with the Doc, or sat with him in the town's cigar shop talking nonsense. The Doc presumably was Earp's only really intimate friend.

"There were many stories about how Earp and the Doc were supposed to have met, and they were all different. The one I've always believed is that once in Wichita the Doc for some unfathomable reason helped Wyatt against a crowd of drunken cowboys, and that Wyatt held that the Doc had saved his life.

"But it was not just because of that that they were friends. They did business together. They gambled together. They could go to a mining camp and each join a different poker table, and twenty-four hours later they would leave with every nickel there was in the camp, and usually with some watches and rings and breloques as well. They were the most impossible boys over cards I've ever seen.

"Both of them always had money, but I believe Wyatt had most. He was more of a business man. The Doc just gambled and won; he never invested money in things. Wyatt bought real estate and building plots all over the place, and wherever he went he always had a heap of papers with him and wrote letters to lawyers and looked after his affairs. In the end he owned building sites and houses throughout the whole of the Wild West. It was quite remarkable. He was a specialist in corner sites. He went to the cattle towns and mining camps early on and had a genius for scenting out which place would become the town's best business corner, and that was the plot he would buy. He owned corner sites in Wichita and Deadwood and Laramie and in many other places, and he used to sit of an evening thumbing through his papers and deeds and insurance policies and looking darned pleased with himself. He could amuse himself that way in the evening by a camp fire. If he became really talkative, he would level a patch of sand, or smooth down the grass, and light a cigar and with the barrel of his pistol draw plans of how some of his houses lay.

"He had an eye for all sorts of transactions. Whenever he came to a new settlement he would see at once what was needed most; whether it was a bar or a gaming saloon or a hotel or a woodyard or a hauliers. He would start any kind of business that would pay. When he was in Deadwood once, he sold firewood. Everyone was searching madly for gold; but when Wyatt arrived there in the autumn, he never bothered about pick and frying pan and washing for gold, but stayed in the town remembering that winter was coming. People thought him a bit queer when they saw him going into the forest and spending all day cutting firewood and stacking it, when the country was stiff with gold you could search for!

"Yet the evening came when Wyatt showed them how to make real money, instead of roaming about looking for gold and gambling away what you found. One winter's day he returned from Laramie, where he had been to play poker and buy a few things and he reached Deadwood just as the north wind began to blow from the Canadian prairies and it became so hellishly cold that nobody could do anything. The town filled up with the gold diggers, who came pouring in as soon as the cold set in, and naturally they began to play poker. Strangely enough Wyatt was not at any table. He must have had enough at Laramie. Yet every day he went to the Silver Dollar bar, where the biggest poker gang sat, and came away looking pleased. Every time he went there, the place was colder and more hellish, until people's breath there was like white funnels that you could have sawn through. On the fourth day the poker players began to curse and swear at O'Neill, the owner, telling him to get some fuel before they froze to death, for no Christian could play cards when it was so cold.

"O'Neill was most unhappy. He had never thought it would be as cold as all that, and it had never occurred to him to get in a stack of firewood to have in readiness. The town was out of wood, and no one would go into the forest to cut timber in that cold; people just lay under bearskins or kept guard on their own wretched stoves. The situation became so hopeless that people had to stop spitting at the stove. O'Neill put up a special notice about that.

"Finally, O'Neill found out that Wyatt had wood, that he was the only one who had, and that it was dear. He went across to Wyatt's through the icy blast and asked what his wood cost, and Wyatt said that as things were in the town the price was now 25 cents a billet. O'Neill was horrified, for that meant that they would burn a dollar's worth every two or three minutes, and he went back to the poker table and said that he must close the bar and ask them to go, for he could no longer heat the place. They asked what firewood cost and O'Neill told them Wyatt's price, but they just shouted that warmth was worth whatever it darned well cost, and that they would pay for it themselves, for they had come to play poker not to save money.

"Wyatt sent an old drunkard he employed across with some billets and said that they must pay cash if they wanted more. They were mad keen to play, though the game was already in its fifth day, so whenever anyone won, he sent for more wood with the money and that let them sit on and continue the game. In that way Wyatt got every penny without ever taking a hand. He just lay on his bearskin smoking cigars, and every now and again he got up and loaded a sledge with as many billets as his old boozer could haul to the Silver Dollar.

"Every seven hours Wyatt put up the price of his wood, but the men paid just the same. They weren't drunk, for nobody could get drunk in that cold, but they had to go on playing. The cold lasted for over a week, and Wyatt sold wood the whole time. The last few billets went for two dollars apiece. That was the eleventh day, and by then the poker players had long beards white with frost and were sucked dry, for the whole kitty they had begun with was then in Wyatt's pocket. He had got their watches and wedding rings as well for the last few billets, but he returned those. He is said to have made 30,000 dollars on that cold snap.

"Doc Holliday and Earp—there are more tales about those two than about anyone else: how they shot, how they won at poker, how they put people in their places. People really went in awe of the Doc; in fact, they trembled a bit, if you just mentioned the name of the little madman. But Earp was always the stout, sterling fellow; he would always help you; he was like other people, he looked after his money and deeds. But both were fabulous characters.

"And one morning when I went into Doc's room with a bottle of whisky that he had asked me in his usual mild way to run and buy for him, there was a tall, fair-haired chap in a black frock coat sitting in his rocking-chair, and the Doc said as I entered:

" 'Bow to Wyatt Earp, else he'll shoot off the tip of your nose.'

"I recognized him at once from when I held his horse that time he got the money for Katie's piano in Dodge City, and I made him a deep bow, almost like the Chinese who lived two blocks from us, but Earp said:

" 'Don't bow, but do your lessons and learn arithmetic. Learn to do sums, and here's a dollar to start on.'

"And he gave me a shiny silver dollar."

12

HOLD-UPS AND COWBOYS

"Wyatt Earp soon had a finger in most things in Tombstone. He began by riding as shotgun with the Bisbee diligence which brought the miners' pay. His brother Virgil was already City Marshal. He was the first of the brothers to come here, and all you need say of Wyatt's brothers, of Morgan who was older and of the two younger ones, Virgil and James, was that they were pleasant copies of him. No more. But no less either—they could shoot pretty well. But they always kept in the background. I can't remember what any of them looked like. Where there was serious trouble and the Earp brothers came prepared to shoot, or if they had just walked in together for a drink at the bar, it was always Wyatt who was in front with the others a bit behind.

"The brothers were alike in one thing, and that was that they could never stay put. It wasn't just Wyatt who was eternally roaming about. Morgan, Virgil and James were always on the move. They went by diligence here and there, prospected for gold, did bits of business, sold horses, gambled, were marshals and police officers. I don't think they had ever been all together in one place until Tombstone, but having assembled there, they stuck together.

"Virgil had originally intended to prospect for silver, but he became City Marshal when some of the townspeople asked him to take it on. He thought that there would always be time enough to look for silver, when he wasn't going about arresting people. He realized that Tombstone was a town on the way up, and so he wrote for his brothers to come. Wyatt wrote, of course, and asked about building plots and property, so as to get an idea if it was the sort of town for him to invest money in. He didn't rely only on his young brother there, but wrote as well to his old friend the Doc whom he knew to be in the town, and that is how it came about that one morning Wyatt was sitting in the Doc's room and I was sent to buy a bottle of whisky.

"Now, afterwards, I have no clear recollection of the order in which things happened. Wyatt was in Tombstone for more than a year and a half, and it would be too much to expect me to remember it all as it happened. I must have been fourteen at the time. Father became quite grand from having both Doc Holliday and Wyatt Earp under his roof, and he went about the town and stalked into Crystal Palace with quite a new dignity. But Wyatt only stayed with us a week or so. After that he and his brothers bought a house on the corner of First and Fremont, strangely enough right next to the Mexican barracks, and there he lived all the time he was in Tombstone.

"There's so much that is just lies and rumour attaching to this Tombstone business, and no one seems rightly to know what Wyatt actually was in Tombstone. Some say that he was sheriff and others that he was City Marshal. But he wasn't either.

"Wyatt was a Republican, and Arizona, it's true, had a Republican governor at that time, but the state was Democrat, and Tombstone was Democrat through and through, and the cattle owners round the town were Democrats. They were mostly Southerners and veterans from the Southern States' army. Wyatt was a Yankee and a Republican, and he could never have been elected to a municipal office. But the Governor appointed him Federal Marshal for Tombstone district, which meant that he had to intervene if the post bags were stolen or the diligence robbed. He had nothing to do with rows in the town, nor with thefts of cattle. Wyatt didn't want the job; he much preferred doing business and had intended to start a diligence line and buy houses and plots, but since his brother Virgil was already City Marshal, he thought it wouldn't be a bad thing if the two brothers were responsible for all order in the district.

"This is where all the fuss and all the divided opinions about Earp originate. People thought it somehow suspicious that Wyatt owned houses and land, that he bought shares in the gaming rooms in Crystal Palace and Occidental, while at the same time he and his brother formed the police power in the town and he himself rode shotgun with the diligence. Father thought it suspect—but remember that father was a South Stater and a cattle man and disliked Wyatt from the beginning, even though he was impressed by knowing him. There was a deep-rooted enmity between those who reared cattle and those who bought them and freighted them east—between South Staters and North Staters, between ranchers and buyers, between cattle and the railways. It was a gulf that ran through the entire West, and father and Wyatt stood on opposite sides of it. Wyatt had people against him from the very start in Tombstone: the cattle men and their cowboys.

"Wyatt ran into trouble at the very beginning.

"He had not been in the town a month before he had his horse stolen. Actually he was more astonished than angry. In almost every town where he had been before, he had been able to trust to his reputation: no one would have dared steal his horse. Shoot at him from behind, yes, or try to pick a bar quarrel with him when backed up by several companions—but not steal his horse.

"He is said to have locked himself in for a whole day and thought it all over, and to have told the Doc that he was beginning to grow old. After this he became watchful and sharper. Till then he had been quite easy-going: he had gone about the town, sat in Crystal Palace and seen to the faro tables and the poker games there and at Occidental, keeping an eye on his interests, or he had sat rocking on a tilted chair outside the cigar shop looking sleepy. But now a dangerous, watchful look had come into his eye.

"People were shot in the town and things were pretty rowdy as they always had been, but Wyatt did not concern himself with that; he was United States Deputy Marshal and murders in the town were nothing to do with him, they were his brother Virgil's province and Wyatt was careful not to interfere. Nor did he let himself get involved in Doc Holliday's tavern rows and rumpuses over women. The Doc never shot anyone in Tombstone, but he drew his revolver once or twice every evening, or threatened to do so, as he sat playing poker, and people became irritated by his murderous looks when it got into the small hours. Wyatt always went away when it looked as though the Doc was going to have a settling of accounts. He did not wish to become involved.

"But you could see that the theft of his horse had destroyed his peace of mind. Every day cowboys would come in to Tombstone from the ranches outside, and sometimes you could see Wyatt just standing in the middle of the street with his hat pulled low over his eyes and the wind playing in his long moustaches, while he stared after some especially unpleasant specimen, usually someone with wide flapping breeches and mother-of-pearl buttons in his hat and Mexican boots, or with big silver spurs with glistening rowels. He would stand and stare, and thoughtfully shift the quid from one side of his moustachioed mouth to the other, then walk on with bowed head and eyes on the ground. It was easy to see that he was vexed and angry.

"Before Wyatt came and began riding with them as shotgun, the diligences to Bisbee and Tucson had been attacked several times, but the attacks ceased once Wyatt took to sitting up on the box beside the driver. Some people, of course, took this to mean that Wyatt had an arrangement with the bandits to leave the diligence alone when he was on the box. To make matters worse, Wyatt quarrelled with the sheriff of the district. It's extraordinary how they were able to make such a mess of things as they did in the West from the very beginning. People came in their thousands, both good and bad, and they drank and they fought, and they built schools and churches, yet one of the first and most important things they had to do always seemed to be to get themselves an administration just like what they had had at home in the eastern states, with politicians who slanged each other and took bribes and pushed their own friends and relatives forward. The sheriff in Tombstone was a chap called Behan and he was in with the cattlemen and cowboys, and when he had to go and hunt anyone who had been up to some devilment, he always swore in a lot of cowboys as deputy marshals and thus made them officers of the law. That infuriated Wyatt, for he knew, as did everyone, that Behan's cowboys stole cattle and robbed diligences in their spare time, and he thought it going a bit far that they should function as police.

"Some months after Wyatt came to Tombstone and was made Marshal the town was full to overflowing and people were being shot and murdered every day. Outside the town lived the ranch-owners, and they wanted to control the entire district and get hold of the mines and all the money there was to be had. In the midst of the turmoil was Wyatt who had had his horse stolen, and there too sat the crazy Doc playing cards. It did not require much for hell to break loose.

"It began when the diligence from Bisbee was held up. It was stuffed with money, for it was carrying the miners' pay from the bank in Bisbee. Nothing was stolen. The ruffians did not get as far as that; but they shot the driver and the man who was riding shotgun instead of Wyatt. They had started searching for the money, but when one of them stuck his head inside the coach, the editor of the *Epitaph*, a man called Clum, who happened to be a passenger and had been made to get out and stand by the side of the road, managed to pull out a little pocket revolver and he shot the man in the backside. It was not much of a shot, for the bullet scarcely pierced the man's trousers, but it made the men, who were masked, think that help had arrived, and they lost their heads and made off. Clum was so astonished that he could not believe his eyes, so he unhitched one of the trace horses and rode bareback into Tombstone, where he rushed into Crystal Palace and told what had happened. Then he dashed to the *Epitaph* and started to write, and came out with a special number about the hold-up before midnight.

"There was a fearful commotion in the town. For several months there had been nothing except Mexicans knifing or shooting each other, and a diligence hold-up with two people killed was just about the biggest thing that could happen in the West next to an Indian rising. The bars and saloons kept open till dawn. People ran about madly questioning each other and the craziest rumours began to circulate. About seven o'clock the next morning O'Shaugnessy, the undertaker, came in with the two bodies on his lorry, and there was a sudden, deathly silence.

"O'Shaugnessy looked like an eternal reminder of death. He always wore a top hat, and his trousers and jacket were too short for him. His arms were like white polished ivory where they protruded from the sleeves, and there was a blue-white cadaverous green tinge to his wrists and cheeks; and he looked as sorrowful as a whipped dog. He might on occasion come into Crystal Palace and drink a glass of whisky and even smile; but his smile was like the silver-plate on a coffin. He was a good business man, and had a special reduced charge for Saturdays and Sundays, which was both humane and clever.

"O'Shaugnessy had his place next door to Nellie's brothel,

and he stopped his lorry outside there to get people to help him carry the corpses in. At this juncture the brothers Earp and Sheriff Behan came up to have a look at O'Shaugnessy's lorry, and it is worth mentioning that Behan came out from Nellie's. He and Wyatt at once began quarrelling about whose responsibility the affair was. Behan insisted that he was sheriff of the entire district, but Wyatt held that he ought to take charge since the hold-up had been an attack on the money, and as this was in a special strong-box protected by the seal of the United States, that made it a matter for the United States' Deputy Marshal. They quarrelled about this, standing one on either side of the lorry as the men took the corpses off and carried them in. Behan advanced a lot of pertinent and complicated arguments, while Wyatt was content to say nothing most of the time, only now and again curtly telling Behan to shut up.

"All this happened in the grey light of daybreak, when people had been on their feet for eighteen or twenty hours and everybody looked wan and exhausted. There was the lorry with the two corpses, and the undertaker looking more like a corpse than the bodies themselves, and then came Behan and Earp and stood quarrelling—it was a bleak and disagreeable morning.

"It could only end in one way: they both rode out after the bandits. Behan spent all morning mobilising a gang of cowboys of sufficiently disreputable appearance and swearing them in as temporary marshals, and that gave him a posse after his own heart. Behan was an intriguer and a thoroughly nasty character, but he did not look like it. He had an innocent childish face which took most people in.

"Wyatt went off with his brothers and Doc Holliday. The Doc had been in bed and asleep and had not got up until the lorry had come rolling in, and it was that which gave impetus to the rumour that it was he who had held up the diligence and that Wyatt was an accomplice and wanted to protect him. It was quite impossible to kill that rumour, and the outcome of the hunt for the bandits only seemed to feed it. For neither Behan nor Earp caught any diligence-robbers, though there were innumerable tracks all round the place where the hold-up had been made. Wyatt and Behan rode out from Tombstone separately, but inevitably they met by the abandoned diligence, and there they stayed and quarrelled for the best part of an hour, and then rode out into the desert, not exactly together, but following the same tracks. That evening Wyatt caught up with a man on a ranch near Convention Mine who had a blown horse turned out to graze and his boots covered with red sand, the same red sand as there was on the road along which the diligence had come. But he had a brother and lots of good friends in Behan's posse which arrived a few minutes later.

"This time Wyatt just gave Behan a long look, then he swore and rode off.

"They could have gone on like that for ever. Wyatt and his brothers and the Doc could have tracked down every one of the men who had taken part in the hold-up, but it would just have turned out that they were cowboys and had Behan to protect them. Wyatt realized that Behan was in on everything the cowboys did and that he received a percentage of the proceeds from all robberies of diligences and thefts of cattle. But Behan and his gang made the same assertion about Earp, and people did not know what to believe.

"After this the two men were mortal enemies; and if the town had been a powder magazine before, it was now a barrel of over-fermented whisky.

"The next thing that happened was that Wyatt found his stolen horse.

"This was in a corral right in the town. He recognized it by a white blaze on its near fore-hock, and when he whistled a signal it had been used to, the horse at once responded. Wyatt went and bought some cigars and sat himself down out of sight to wait for whoever came to fetch the horse. He had to smoke five or six of his cigars, before his patience was rewarded.

"The man who came and began to saddle the horse was some-one he did not know, a foreman cowboy called Rattlesnake Smith. He had got the name in the days when he used to peddle whisky at the buffalo grounds and in the railway construction camps. He sold a darned strong brand of whisky, which every-body liked and with which no other person's could compete. One day, however, when he was unloading his whisky off a waggon to set up his booth, one of the casks fell off the top of the load and burst open. There was a crowd standing round at the time, and one of them found a string of five or six rattlesnake heads inside the burst cask.

"There was a fearful commotion. At first Smith said that he had no idea how the snake-heads had got there, and then some of the men knocked a hole in another of the casks and, sure enough, there were snake-heads in that too. They then knocked holes in every cask Smith had, and, darn me, but there were rattlesnakes in every one, mostly skeletons with skulls and vertebrae and a little skin. The men beat Smith up, big as he was; they kicked him out and promised to shoot him on the spot if they ever heard that he was again selling whisky on the prairie. He disappeared south to Arizona and became foreman on a ranch, but I know that afterwards there were plenty of buffalo-hunters and railroad men who regretted having chucked him out, for whatever way they looked at it, nobody else had ever had whisky to touch his.

"It was this Rattlesnake Smith who had stolen the horse, and that fact was further confirmation for Wyatt that the cowboys were all against him.

"Throwing his cigar away, he walked up to Smith just as he was throwing the saddle across the horse's back and asked:

" 'Where did you get that fine horse?'

"Smith thought for half a second, then his hand flew towards the holster on his hip; but before it was half way there Earp had given him a tap on the head with the barrel of his pistol. Let me just remind you here that in the Wild West well-behaved people never struck with the butts of their pistols, as you sometimes hear or see on films. If a man took his pistol by the barrel and struck with the butt, the blow would have killed an ox, and that was not what was intended when you hit someone with a revolver, at least not always. Earp had his pistol lying on his palm with the butt up on his arm and the barrel lying along his fingers, and he dealt you a blow with that, which always did what he intended. Having knocked Rattlesnake Smith out, he then hung him on a nail in the wall, took his horse and went to fetch his brother Virgil, so that Smith could be handed over to the proper authorities.

"Smith was just coming to when Wyatt and his brother returned, and they took him between them and flung him into the lock-up.

"By the morning, news of what had happened had reached the ranches. To lay hands on a cowboy was to insult them all, so

now it was open war between the Earp brothers and the cowboys, and between the town and the ranches. Things began to
happen. One night the cashier at Convention Mine was shot and
all the wage money taken. Diligences began to be held up once
more and Sheriff Behan went about saying that this was Doc
Holliday's doing, and that he must stop him. Naturally it was
Earp he was aiming at.

"The whole thing was most disturbing, for anyone with any
sense realized that the cowboys and ranchers wished to be rid of
the mine-owners and thus own all Tombstone and control the
entire district. The ranchers would gladly have seen the prospectors and mine-owners in hell, for they wanted all the ground
for their cattle. The worst of the ranchers was an old chap called
Clanton who lived with his sons on a ranch about two miles
from the town. He was a dreadful person. Appalling stories
were told about him, but I don't know how much was true. It
was said that he and his sons and the ranch's cowboys had once
fallen upon twenty Mexican smugglers and slaughtered them like
pigs and taken everything they had. One little lad had escaped,
and old man Clanton and his son Ike had hunted the boy through
the hills for a whole day, before they caught him and cut his
throat. What I do know, though, is that they were unimaginably
rough and ruthless, for I sometimes saw them in Tombstone.
When they entered a bar, they would turn everyone else out,
the old man lashing out with a buffalo hide whip; they raped the
barmaids on the tables and altogether behaved like swine.
Clanton had four boys, and every such evening ended by his
thrashing them, then collapsing and falling asleep.

"All the ranch-owners hated the mine-owners and the gold
diggers. They wanted nothing but cattle. They were furious
because a town had grown up, at there being decent hotels
instead of the hellish pigstyes they liked to frequent. They were
wild at everything around them that was unconnected with
cattle. They wanted to have the land to themselves, to be free to
ride down into Mexico and rustle cattle, to steal from the Indians,
to live as they liked, without laws. Behan was their man. They
took him out to their ranches and bribed him with good food and
Mexican wine and flung him some neat little Mexican girl, who
knew a special trick or two, and thus they had him snared.

"Now that Wyatt had beaten up one of them hell was loose.

"The whole town realized that, and a general depression set in. People sat silent and gloomy at their tables as they ate. Deathly quiet reigned at the poker tables. The place was like a ship about to sink. Everyone realized that the cowboys would be out for vengeance, that they would vent upon the town all the venom they had been storing up during the two years the mines had been working. Everyone was tense and nervous, and people stood talking quietly at street corners.

"But Wyatt was calm. He had a favourite spot, which was outside the cigar shop opposite Crystal Palace. Strategically it was a good place, for from there he could see four streets. He always sat rocking on a chair with his feet on one of the columns that held up the roof of the veranda. He sat there waggling his feet and rocking his chair at the same time, so that it was never still. When anyone passed, he always stood up and greeted him, and he even did the same when the girls from Nellie's came waggling along.

"Things remained thus for several days. People were nervous, and Wyatt sat and rocked on his chair and smoked cigars. And nothing happened. There was thunder in the air.

"On the third day a crowd of cowboys came riding into the town. They raised a hellish cloud of dust in Allen Street. They knew, of course, where Wyatt sat awaiting them, and the whole group, ten or twelve of them in a bunch, rode full gallop towards him, and when they were just in front of him, they reined in their horses so that they reared up and that made the dust even worse, and then they turned and rode to the rail in front of Crystal Palace and dismounted there.

"The cloud of dust hung round the street corner for a couple of minutes or so, and when it had settled there was Wyatt sitting exactly as he always did, rocking on his chair with his feet on the wooden pillar and smoking a cigar. It was as if he had not seen them.

"I remember that well, for my father and I stood and watched it; and before he turned and walked home with me, father said softly:

"'Now, the devil!'"

13

DAMN WASHINGTON

Hassayamper had made himself tired and been forced to go to bed. He had had too many highballs and the Apache queen had grown nervous and had whispered to him and finally helped him up to bed, while we others sat in discreet silence.

When Margareta and I had gone to bed in our bungalow, opened the big glass doors and thrust back the shutters slightly so that the desert moon drew a ribbon of white up to the edge of the rug, I lay and thought of Earp. Softly I said:

"He sat at his camp fire and thumbed through his business papers. He sat alone by a fire out on the prairie, while his horse grazed, and he dreamed of his property and his sites, and the jackals howled out in the night and the Apache lay and waited for the dawn perhaps in order to kill him. And he just thought of his street corners and his interest rates and dividends, and had his pistol ready and a Remington rifle. Perhaps that was how it all came into being. The Wild West, I mean. The whole U.S.A."

From outside came a faint creaking sound that told us that a slight night breeze had come down off the Dragon Mountains and was turning the vane of the water pump.

I got up and lit a cigar, and we sat and talked about how the transition between town and country was different there than at home in Sweden. The towns did not peter out and become farming land, nor a forested wilderness, but turned into a timeless landscape where man had merely scrabbled with his hands and fingers and left traces of his despair and his struggle.

About the drive-in cinemas into which cars turned off the asphalt highway and lined up like cows beside the milking machine, while those inside, fast-rooted to their wheels and levers and upholstery, stared through the glass windscreens at a celluloid story.

About the telegraph poles in the towns, rough, unplaned and grey even when planted in front of the polished stone palaces of the banks and of the fifteen-storeyed stores of the Western cities—reminders that these laboriously built towns were mere excrescences, swellings on the thin telegraph line.

About the display windows of the sports shops in all the towns, especially Abercrombies in New York, and the romance attaching to the shot-gun and the fishing gear and the imaginative accessories designed to suggest hardship and fatigue. Always the same aspiration on the part of people who lived in a hygienic, clean smelling atmosphere like a hairdresser's: to mortify the flesh in swamps beside lakes in the autumn and to live in log cabins that from outside look like blockhouses and inside are like gleaming model kitchens.

They too sat by camp fires thumbing through deeds and papers.

That led us back to Wyatt Earp who slaughtered the buffalo and tried to exterminate them, so that the Indians could no longer live on their hunting grounds; Wyatt Earp who prepared the way for the telegraph poles and railways and prospectors, for the school mistresses and Carnegie's people's libraries, trams and oil derricks, and art museums and the Methodist University, the billiard saloons and gymnasia, and the service stations and drive-in cinemas.

But then—there was that November snow storm the time we drove from Kansas City through Missouri, crossed the Mississippi at Mark Twain's Hannibal and so northwards across the plain. The storm turned the vast prairie into a narrow wind-tunnel, and the blast was the hand of death pressing on radiator and windscreen. All of a sudden we in the car stopped talking. We could still taste the bacon and eggs and strong coffee we had had at the last halting place, which had been a mechanized dream of food production and distribution, of comfort and well-being, but we dared not speak, for we felt how helpless we were in our tin-plate vehicle. On the wireless Perry Como was singing about Christ and girls and mother and home, and then the wind and the snow took us and spun us round thrice on the icy road, and we sat and waited for death, but instead we were playfully deposited, safe and sound, in a field.

We managed to get back to another milk-bar which was filled with noisy people and police who had stuck in drifts, and men who lolled in armchairs while the storm roared, and they had talked of the price of building plots and real estate.

That is how it must have been.

Or the thunderstorm that fell upon us out of the blazing heat in Louisville, when we were only ten steps away from Brown's Hotel and had just looked into the sky and remarked that it was a lovely day. The rain was like a dark blue cataract round us; the thunder seemed to explode inside our heads, and the avenue was a place transformed, a sluiced corridor for catastrophe and horrors and people who shouted and clung tight to the door-handles of the closed shops to prevent themselves being swept away.

Yet in Brown's bar where we took refuge, were men sitting in deep chairs between pictures of Derby winners and thorough-breds from Kentucky's blue grass, talking about corner sites and plots and real estate prices, and whether it might not be a good idea to invest your money further west, that according to what they had heard a chap saying in the club the night before, the outlying part down by Houston and out at Phoenix ought to be good. Brown's bar was nothing but a camp fire at which people dreamed of money in the west.

They were all Wyatt Earps dreaming of things and investments in the west, toying with the romance of adventure; and their bars and club chairs were the warmth and temporary security of those camp fires of long ago: the prairie was to be settled, there were to be law, a real estate code and rights of property and town-planning. And across the prairie, like taut strings, lay the humming telegraph lines and the motor highways, and the thin layer of the towns, the hairdresser's saloons, the greasing stations for motor cars which were called lubricatoriums, and the laboratories and the Methodist University. It all lay close to the frontier with the west, with the next territory to which no one had yet gone, but which you could already dream of in-vesting money in.

In the morning we got up to another day with those rheumatic and allergic adventurers and went among them, eager to believe that things were as we had thought. Twisted Titus from the fruit farms of California with his confident smile; taciturn Chuck who had once shot his horse outside the town before entering it; the white-bearded professor whom the South Seas had washed up there, and who was busy pottering with his second oldest Ford and thinking out details to add to his festival play about Tomb-stone: the passion play about the adventure of Tombstone that they were always playing at.

In the bright light of day, round the swimming pool and beside the Apache queen, she who had been there before any of the others, we became sober again, however, and saw them merely as scatter-brained rheumatics and limited invalids begging sunshine and money to live by.

But then came the twilight and dinner and the fire in the hearth, and again they looked as though they were resting round a camp fire on their journey towards the horizon and the rebirth of their civilization in another place: always riding west, ever west-wards. Like in an old cowboy's song.

There was nothing adventurous about the events of the few days that remained of our stay on Lazy M. Titus and Hassayamper spent more and more time closeted together. Judah and the Professor were summoned to attend their conferences, and it appeared inevitable that Hassayamper would yet see the ranch debased to a tourist place. Of the better class, of course. Titus was always taking me confidentially round a corner and whispering and saying that naturally it would not be like what Hassayamper feared and imagined, but only the very best. Foreign ambassadors to U.S.A. were to come to Lazy M and rest and ride over the cactus plain, and so would "executives" and star models who had married the big bosses of textile concerns. Titus' eyes shone as he told us all this, and then he sighed over Hassayamper and the dairies and the milk and the cattle subsidies, and said that to run a ranch just as a ranch was to make a serf of yourself.

"Damn Washington," he said, and shook his fist at the east. "God damn Washington."

The affaire between Mary Lou and Chisholm also developed and with as little surprise. It was the same with her as with the Professor's daughter, she too had white bumps on her knees when she crossed her legs, and it was impossible to stop watching the play of soft sinews and thin muscles in her arms and legs. She was appetising and clinked with bracelets and chains, and her shoes were usually like lines drawn with Indian ink across the bones of her feet, yet a ghastly thought kept obtruding; when she sat down you caught a glimpse of the black or white or green of a petticoat with embroidery like a ham frill, and the effect was as though it were all detached and removable, as though her legs were false ones, bought at a store. In fact, was there a body?

The legs of these women of the West are ready-made, bought

at stores by their mothers so that they are all alike, and they are bought with shoes already on, even the low-heeled ones which are cut low to the big toe joint, a ridiculously plain place on the human body which they yet manage to fill with innuendo.

What progress were they making with their love affaire?

They were both, as it were, engaged in a game of bridge to which there were many spectators standing behind them, winking and approving and chuckling with them in a gushing sort of way, and they were passing so as to be on the safe side.

But it was also quite safe and unhurried, especially when you remembered that Mary Lou had previously been married to a brute. Naturally it was not passion Mary Lou sought, for she was alone and thus wanted security: not just the security of the bird in the nest, but all the security there was, and it was that you were getting close to, when you heard the clink from her arms and saw her lace-up shoes twine voluptuously round each other and became aware of the ham frills. It was the same in the bars in New York where all the divorced women sat, hair prettily blue-washed, silly red marks on their cigarettes, and lovely legs gripping on to their stools as they chatted with the bar-tender: you felt that the air was charged, that here was a camp fire, a place where people had a second's frantic enjoyment before rushing on, and you looked at the flesh beneath the dress at the back where it formed a slight fold by the arm-pit.

But it was never like that; they were never aware of their legs or of their arms; all they knew was that you ought to sit with your legs roughly like that while you waited upon security.

Mary Lou felt that; she was engaged in a big, model play, and there was so much she had to take into consideration: her daughter Ysabel and her father Judah and her grandfather Hassayamper, and the fact that one day half of Lazy M would be hers and Chisholm's.

I watched Chisholm sometimes when he was not aware of it, and mentally tried to place him in his European setting: I could see him in a commercial hotel in a country town; there was a terrace and an orchestra playing, and the waitresses' shoes crunched on the gravel as they walked to and from the kitchen, and he had a car and told you how fast he had driven coming there and how by insisting on his rights he had almost done the man who sold him the car, and that he must go and ring up the "little woman" and that they had two kids at home, and that that waitress wasn't at all bad and he would not mind a tumble with her damn it, and he had a book full of orders, pity he couldn't get home to his wife and kids, but here was the girl coming at last, so now we could find out what time she finished.

Chisholm could have had all that in his make-up; but there he was in Arizona beneath the desert sun paying court to Mary Lou, biding his time and passing as though engaged in a rather leisurely game of bridge.

Everyone smelt nice, that too was part of Lazy M and the cactus desert. The sun was like a glaring hard cover over your entire existence. The swimming pool intensified the heat. When you came out after cooling yourself there, the drops of water left on your red shoulders hurt like bits of glass. But everybody had a nice smell, so had all Lazy M, the whole of Arizona; that was life's first commandment; do not take the mustiness of your body among your fellow-men; in security and fragrance we can make shift with ourselves and each other. That did not fit with the commercial travellers' hotel, and I narrowed my eyes and had another look at Chisholm, just as he was about to ask the waitress when she finished work: the sweat was exuding from his jacket as asphyxiatingly as from a skunk.

In the sociable, noisy atmosphere of the swimming pool at Lazy M. Chuck was as reserved and uncommunicative as elsewhere, and when we saw him on the prairie, he was always coming from somewhere or riding to somewhere; he was the confidant of the mornings, in harmony with the parched and drowsy afternoon, habitual brother of the dusk, a good friend of night and day. There was something of Wyatt Earp about him, wherever he rode and in whatever chair he sat by our camp fire. His pale blue eyes would peer at some torn-off cactus branches to see whether a car had driven too close there, or look up at the Dragon Mountains to see whether wind or rain were on the way: those were atavistic habits that had struggled to the surface through a couple of generations and the telegraph wires, palatial banks, drive-in cinemas and chromium-plated milk-bars. We neither saw his wife nor heard her mentioned; she was and remained a mystery. Was she a cripple or disreputable?—we never dared ask; but there was so much that was mysterious about Chuck, the quid of tobacco under his upper lip and his whiskers and his stiff, jerky way of walking across the splintered stone.

"What sort of weather will we have in the morning," we might ask.

Chuck would squirt a dark jet of tobacco juice at a stone with a juicy sound, jerk his hat back off his forehead, stick both thumbs into his broad belt and stare up at the mountains.

"Well now, that's a question, that is," he would say.

That would be all the answer we would get then. Now and again throughout the forenoon we would see Chuck standing gazing up at the mountains. Then, several hours after asking our question, when we had already retreated to our bungalow to escape the worst of the midday heat, he would come and knock and shift his quid across to the other side of his mouth and say:

"It'll be a bit cooler than today."

And it would be.

Sometimes he would stoop down as he walked across the courtyard and pick up something, look at it and sling it away and laugh to himself or look thoughtful. The object might be a nail, a piece of dry sheep's droppings—for Judah and the Professor had made Hassayamper experiment with sheep—or a nut that had dropped off a car: everything was a sign to him; he read it and smiled or was surprised; he had his amusement in knowing all these things, in the interpretation of mirages above the mountains, of broken cactus branches, of nails and nuts.

Yet behind the façade of his cowboy's hat and tobacco quid and high-heeled boots he was really a plumber, and once he took one of the spurs off his boots and with it he drew in the sand of the yard the main plan of the drainage system of Tombstone school.

Then we heard something about the merry Slattery: he had once broken away from the ranch and his cattle, and for ten years he had been gone driving a Greyhound bus.

That was the same as driving a diligence.

He had driven his diligence, been one of the lines across the prairie, the mountain deserts and the wilds in which the towns and palatial banks were just excrescences. Strictly speaking it was behind him that we had driven westwards on our separate ways and we recognized him in various Greyhound bus drivers we remembered: the one who had turned a drunk off in the middle of Wyoming one Sunday morning, and the one who had gone and bought an expensive box of chocolates for a humpbacked girl in her teens, whose pink best dress smelt of seldom-opened wardrobe and who found sitting difficult because of her hump; her face was made old by the tension in her body, and her mother could scarcely manage her any more. They were laughing, placid creatures, the men who drove the diligences westward; and sometimes they came and were friendly to the passengers over coffee in the milk-bars, those camp fires on the way. There was Slattery in them all, and now he had stopped to loose his gaiety among the cattle and the boys who are called cowboys.

Each evening we walked out to the cactus that looked like an old man, and sometimes we would hear Hobo singing without rightly knowing where he was, though we presumed he must be in the stables, busy with some horse that had become his favourite. He sang his songs:

"Carry on, carry on, little ploughboy
And dream you are a real cowboy. . . ."

It sounded infinitely melancholy. Hobo was grieved because he was only cook.

We sat round our camp fire in Hassayamper's armchairs. The others too, were there to listen; some kept coming and going, but Margareta and I were always there. Sometimes Slattery made faces behind Hassayamper's back, trying to make us laugh. Hassayamper was always dressed in a thin black suit and wore the same narrow, black, bow-tie. The others wore cowboy checks.

The Professor kept reverting to the subject of the Helldorado and insisting that it was high time the details were worked out. Slattery laughed, Chuck nodded gravely at everything the Professor said. In the end it was decided that I was to be a cowboy and bandit, and that Margareta should be one of the sirens in Crystal Palace. We became enthusiastic about it all, and I thought of Hobo's song: perhaps I was just a ploughboy, but I could always dream and play.

Such were the pleasant thoughts with which I fell asleep by our camp fire on the prairie, protected by glass windows and with the pleasurable certainty that it would be pleasantly cool in the morning for I had remembered to set the thermostat.

14

HANGED BY MISTAKE

Back in Tombstone life resumed its former placid course. We went to Mary Lou's for iced coffee in the afternoons, and I spent a lot of time poring over the *Epitaph*'s old files. Titus would shuffle down from his room above, and himself become interested as he tried to help me lift big, heavy, bound volumes of back numbers. We stirred up the dust and became so horribly dirty, that you felt revolted when, eventually, you emerged into the sunlight.

I had gone to the files to read about the revolver battle between Wyatt Earp and the Clanton brothers, but I never got to that. I became fascinated by the snippets of news. It was like starting to look up something in a dictionary or encyclopaedia and putting the book back on the shelf after reading about lots of other things instead.

It was hot in the *Epitaph*'s big room with its large, dreary, nut-brown tables and scissors and tins of paste. There were two old compositors setting by hand in the depths of the room, but they were grim old chaps and not to be drawn into conversation. I always felt sleepy in there, which was a pity because I had intended to read through year after year and really study the thing; but as it was, I could only manage the smaller items.

I never regretted that though. Tombstone emerged lifesize from those little snippets. It is the small things that are alive in newspapers. Leaders and large-scale reportage on famine, solitary lightships and worthy pillars of society . . . no, no. It is only the unimportant trifles that have significance years afterwards. The widow cuts out the funeral notice with its few lines of verse and carries it in her bag, and engagement announcements lie yellowing in pocketbooks.

The things I read were those at the foot of the columns:

"An Indian woman gave birth to a child in the big bush along the road to San Pedro yesterday afternoon. She had no one to help her, but managed perfectly. A number of the curious were drawn to the spot. Those who were there judged the child to be of astonishingly small weight, but otherwise well-shaped. They named it Pedro and made a collection that brought in fifteen dollars and twenty-two cents plus a gold tooth."

"Eight barrels of beer were delivered yesterday to Mr. Martin Costello's saloon, so there is no need to fear thirst in the immediate future.

"A citizen of this town yesterday morning twice fainted in Baron's hairdressing saloon while being shaved. He had just ridden in from Crittenden and had drunk a glass of cold beer, which is presumed to have caused his indisposition. After being shaved, he returned to the bar."

"The Can-can Club reports that it has got sour milk today."

"A citizen, well esteemed in sporting and betting circles, by name Portuguese Joe, unaccountably swooned in front of Crystal Palace late last night."

"Our old friend Pat Holland has informed us in a letter that after his last stay in the territorial gaol in Yuma he also spent some time in the asylum in Los Angeles, but that he now feels quite restored and ready to resume his former activities as professional gambler in Tombstone."

"After the Rev. J. M. Donelly, an itinerant preacher who some weeks ago edified the public on the vacant plot behind the Chinese quarter, was found drunk the day before yesterday in the stable beside Nellie Cashman's establishment, this exponent of the gospel has decided to break off his crusade against Satan in Tombstone and return next year."

"The unusually large rattlesnake which was encountered and killed in the home of a Mexican woman by some of the leading business men of our town who wish to remain anonymous, has been stuffed and is to be seen in Fred Clark's saloon in Allen Street."

"An Indian boy with six fingers on either hand and six toes on each foot aroused considerable interest yesterday evening outside Crystal Palace and occasioned a lively exchange of bets among the patrons of that place of refreshment."

"The hubbub that yesterday disturbed many citizens had its origin in the Chinese quarter, where they were interring to the customary instrumental music, Too Yen, who, as our readers already know, was bitten to death by a sow last week."

"There is no woman on the American stage with greater

talent for depicting violent passions than Miss Jenny Jeffrey-Lewis who will appear this evening at the Birdcage Theatre in *Forget Me Not*, for the benefit of the town burial fund."

"Nellie Cashman's will be closed this evening to honour the memory of Señorita Carmelita Jimenez, a lady who for some years had been attached to the place of entertainment and who on Wednesday took her life by consuming two tablespoonfuls of rat poison."

"John MacPherson O'Neill, a gentleman who has honoured our town with his presence for the last few weeks and who claims to be the descendant of a line of Irish kings, occasioned considerable nervousness on Allen Street yesterday afternoon by shooting the cigars out of the mouths of several passers-by with a new Buntline revolver he had just bought off a cowboy. . . ."

Tombstone Epitaph had no literary critic—not because there were no books in the town but because American dailies had not then taken to having one. But there was a sort of literary criticism: *Epitaph* had an old decayed Oxford student who had originally come out West as an out-of-work actor giving poetry recitals and who had stayed in Tombstone for ten years with the vague intention of one day getting out of bed before noon and starting to prospect for gold. He never managed it, but he became more or less permanently attached to the *Epitaph* and wrote about the funeral orations pronounced up on Boot Hill. He didn't write about the funeral itself—a reporter did that—just about the speech.

Although of common occurrence, funerals were great events in Tombstone—and they reckoned on two or three good ones a week if things were right. *Epitaph* sent two representatives to all funerals with any pretensions—a reporter and this old Oxford man whose name was Carruthers and who criticized the speech made by the parson or one of the pillars of local society, a director of the mine or a politician.

Carruthers was uncompromising as a critic. No one escaped. He kowtowed to none. If it was a weak speech, he said so. Nor did he refrain from criticizing the clergy when he thought they had expressed themselves obscurely or unctuously:

"The oration with which the Rev. James Higginbotham of the Episcopalian Church saw fit to accompany Jesiah F. Monahan's last journey to Boot Hill was so full of misrepresentation and falsehood, that it should be recorded as the weakest ever to have been pronounced over a bier in Tombstone. It concluded, moreover, with a number of guesses about conditions in the next world of which the Rev. Higginbotham presumably knows less than others in our community, especially when in the condition in which he was during the obsequies."

Carruthers came to life in those columns: I imagined him as a man with a coarsened face, which had once been good-looking, and that he had probably been left fatherless early and sent to Oxford with the blessings of a young and pretty Mama, whose money he had soon gone through in travelling up to London and visiting the Empire promenade: a scoffer with despair hidden deep within him. I traced his pen elsewhere than in those criticisms of funerals. Although in the account it just said "our reporter", it must have been he who attended the opening of the new barber's saloon in Occidental Hotel and was promised free service there as long as he should live in Tombstone for having christened it "Occidental Tonsorial Parlour".

During the 'seventies and 'eighties Tombstone was involved in squabbles with its neighbours as to which should be the seat of the county court for Cochise County. Tombstone won—though it has since lost the honour, Bisbee now being the county town. For a couple of years *Epitaph* carried leaders abusing the town's rivals and lauding Tombstone itself. For a period of several months someone marked in blue pencil in the margins who had written what, presumably something to do with paying for contributions, and there Carruthers figures as the author of a couple of leaders on this question—which really amounted to which was the finest town in south-eastern Arizona.

"If a town can have three or four banks of faro going every evening along with a score of poker tables, if it has inexhaustible mines, one of the finest theatres in the West, and the largest bar in the West, and if that town conducts four or five funerals in great style every week, has the most expensive hearse (15,000 dollars) west of the Mississippi and the only one with rounded glass corners, and if it has three murderers in its jail awaiting trial—then it is a successful town and the natural seat for the court and administration of justice in Cochise County. . . ."

The shooting was far less important than one would think. What counted was the trials. Tombstone was a town where one and all were amateur lawyers and had acquired some of the shrewdness characteristic of those who have delved a bit into the world of paper and codes. Everybody had his own views on the finer legal points in the trials, and *Epitaph* daily received letters of astounding technical knowledge concerning mistakes made at the last murder trial or drawing attention to especially good bits in the defence counsel's speech.

The inevitable corollary to the most interesting trials was the execution. When there was a hanging, *Epitaph* increased the number of its pages and gave an almost minute by minute description of the condemned person's last hours.

As *Epitaph* described them hangings must have been extra-ordinary spectacles, with a unique ceremonial, the keynote of which was that the sheriff and the delinquent deliberately behaved as in a drawing-room game for men, calling each other by their Christian names and being exceedingly polite and obliging, while the entire community looked on: it was a sort of magical rite, an exclusive and intimate circle where everything was as it should be and no one was agitated, apparently not even he who was to be hanged.

Everybody was expected to do his job and play his part, and for anyone to act out of character would have been like cheating at cards. The man to be hanged was never a bogey-man, he was the chap they had been playing poker with some evenings before or having a whisky with at the bar. He was brought out from the adobe gaol behind the county court house, was there in the midst of them, nodding to them all with the composure every-body expected of him. He would exchange a few words with his friends while being prepared for dying and nobody seemed to realize how ghastly it all was: the bandage across his eyes, the bit of rope round his knees so that he shouldn't kick, the hands tied behind his back.

Epitaph began its account twenty-four hours before the hanging, and sometimes it even produced a special number in the early morning, an hour or so before the execution, to tell people what sort of a night the condemned had spent. The menu of his last meal was given in a frame on the front page. That last meal was a peculiar social phenomenon in Tombstone, for usually it was not just a few friends and the sheriff who partook, but also all the notabilities and pillars of society who might not even have known the condemned or had anything to do with him; it was really one of the grandest functions of the season and the most exclusive thing to which anybody could be invited.

The condemned were always allowed to choose the menu, and as they were often gamblers or had made money holding up diligences and grown accustomed to choice food at Occidental or Nellie Cashman's, they were always very creditable menus. The food was taken to the prison in silver dishes by the Occidental's waiter. One dish there always was, whether the condemned had ordered it or not, and that was oysters. Oysters were the speciality of the people of Tombstone, they and buffalo tongue, not because people particularly liked them nor yet out of snobbishness, but because they acted as a symbol of the town's industry and greatness: the oysters came either from Cheasepeake Bay on the east coast or from San Francisco, they were expensive and difficult to transport, but the fact that Tombstone could always sport oysters showed how rich and go-ahead it was and what splendid communications it had. They never had oysters in Bisbee.

One of the last ceremonies was the shaving and attiring. The prison always provided the condemned with a neat black suit for his last day, and in those brand new clothes he was buried. That cost the prison up to 200 dollars a hanging, but it was one of Tombstone's traditions. In the morning before he put on his suit the barber came from Occidental and with him an assistant carrying his equipment. A number of the leading lights also attended this ceremony, sitting chatting with the condemned man and giving him a cigar to smoke while the barber shaved him: thus they maintained to the very end the pretence that it was all a parlour game.

What perhaps confirms the impression that those accounts in the *Epitaph*'s columns are not made up or larded with the reporter's own invention is the fact that they do not record any remarkable last words or grim jest on the threshold of death. Nothing would have been more natural had they done so, yet there is nothing of the kind in those reports. They seem genuine. It was not a question of being jocular and superior, or of defying death, but of behaving decently and properly as though the whole affair was of no real significance.

However, they were not expected to keep silent altogether.

They had to greet people and preferably proffer some remarks.

"It's sunny, gentlemen—almost too broiling, you might call it," one is recorded as saying.

Several of these remarks are characterized by a facetious, melancholy elegance in the choice of words. One greeted the crowd assembled round the gallows to see him hanged with a word or two of Spanish mixed in:

"Hullo, *hombres*. I believe you're quaking a bit already."

Another, gravely regarding the throng, said:

"This will be an experience by which you can all benefit."

Some last remark of a religious nature was usual; this was mostly a request for Christian burial.

Nowhere in the *Epitaph*'s columns was there a deliberately macabre jest, even though for many years it had a column called "Death's Doings". There was so much shooting that not every death could make news, so the others were lumped together under a vignette of a smoking revolver and two upturned soles of boots. Beneath were recorded the Mexicans who had shot each other, the horse thieves who had quarrelled with fatal results, the prostitutes who had been stabbed to death in neighbouring towns; the unknown old prospectors found in some cranny among the rocks, burned and scalped by the Apache.

Death's doings. There was also a bartender who had happened to be standing too near a barrel of whisky when it exploded as a result of excessive fermentation.

But never a facetious remark, never a boastful jibe at death: death was treated like whisky and poker, part of a man's social equipment, something requiring ceremony and form which all must know, just as they had to know the movements, the grips and the right words when taking their seats at a poker table or offering a stranger a drink in Crystal Palace.

From the low wooden building housing the *Epitaph* I walked up Allen Street and into the old Birdcage Theatre, through the auditorium and up behind the stage where the old hearse was kept—the most expensive hearse west of the Mississippi. I had been there before and seen it, but had never noticed that the glass at the corners was rounded. It was. Carruthers had described it correctly in his leader on Tombstone's greatness and might.

I also went to inspect the old knaggy tall telegraph pole outside the house which once housed Tombstone's pride, the honour it had lost after only a few years' enjoyment, the Cochise Circuit Court. On that pole were hanged those they lynched, the ones the law never dealt with. At the bar in Crystal Palace I had been told of ten, fifteen who had hung from that pole in the town's heyday, but I think that was a lie. I only found two mentioned in the *Epitaph*, though a number of others had pretty close shaves.

One was called Heath and the other George Johnson. Johnson was rather interesting.

Johnson's personality slowly emerged from the various reports which began with the *Epitaph* itself in 1879. He was mentioned several times in 1880 as one of the few who had been so drunk as to have necessitated the intervention of the law. When he appeared before old Judge Rowlandson, he was obviously not cheeky, but absurdly dignified and using big words as he begged pardon for things of which he was quite innocent, but which he asserted he had done when drunk.

"I am sorry, Your Honour, if I turned the town a bit topsy-turvy," said George Johnson with a pleasant laugh, but the reporter remarks that Johnson had not turned anyone but himself topsy-turvy and that the town's City Marshal—this was before Earp's time—had taken him in charge merely to prevent him injuring himself.

Then there were more serious reports about him. One evening he had entered Crystal Palace after several times approaching its swing doors and turning back, and once inside he had cleared his throat and taken up position midway between the bar and the big poker table, his legs wide apart. No one had bothered about him, as it was just imagined that he was drunk as usual. This time, however, he had produced a revolver and aimed at the bar, evidently intending to shoot an empty whisky bottle which happened to be standing there. Although he was only a few yards from the bottle, he missed badly and the bullet hit the cash register into which old red-cheeked, pomaded Smiling Jim was just about to put some ten-dollar bills—the fact that it was a modern cash register from Dayton, Ohio, is specially mentioned. The bullet released some mechanism with the result that the drawer with the money shot out and hit Smiling Jim in the stomach with a great wallop.

The only damage George Johnson did was thus indirect, in that the till banged the bartender in the stomach, and before George had managed to point his revolver at the roof, obviously intending to fire another shot, he was struck a hard blow between the eyes by Smiling Jim who, despite his age and his obesity, had agilely vaulted the bar.

Johnson was taken unconscious to the calaboose and, when he came to a couple of days later and found himself standing before Judge Rowlandson, he begged pardon with a little laugh for having "stirred up the boys in Crystal Palace a bit". He hinted that he had been in a savage mood.

Following George Johnson's career from issue to issue, as it was recorded in those yellowed columns, I realized that George was Tombstone's first romancer. Nothing was ever said of how he earned his living. Nor did that matter: he was the daydreamer. If he had lived nowadays he would have spent his time at the cinema, worshipping in the temple of those who are afraid of life. But he actually lived in the Wild West and wanted to be wild too. He dreamed of being a cowboy. He deceived himself: he had never stirred up the boys in Crystal Palace—a fifteen-year-old cowboy could have scared them better, at any rate hit the whisky bottle. He had just walked in and tried to be adventurous and been given a humiliating knock-out from the barman, a thing which was always regarded as particularly degrading in the Wild West, not because barmen were weak creatures, but because they never struck you unless you really were behaving badly and also were an insignificant runt whom nobody could respect.

And George Johnson had been knocked-out while holding a pistol in his fist! He must have been dead, socially.

Then for several months there was no mention of him. He must have roamed the streets of Tombstone withdrawing further and further into his inferiority complex. Did he get money sent him by a Mama in one of the eastern states? In his conceited stupidity he still made much of himself. He bought new revolvers, which fact was reported in ironical terms in *Epitaph*'s society column. He walked to and fro along Allen Street with his thumbs stuck inside a cartridge belt.

Up to that point I had thought him a youth, a stripling who had come west for the summer. Then suddenly he appeared in a civil case. He had failed to provide for his spouse and children, as the report of the trial put it, and had been taken to court by his wife, Nancy Independence Johnson. That made Judge Rowland-son annoyed with him and while the entire court laughed—in those days, the heat being what it was, you were allowed to take beer into the public seats—he told Johnson that he ought to get himself a job instead of walking about swanking outside Crystal Palace.

After that George Johnson disappears for several months. A short notice about a diligence horse which fell in the corral provided the information that he had got a job with the Bisbee diligence—not as coachman or spare-driver but as watchman at the line's depot in Tombstone, where spare wheels and shafts and harness were kept. The notice was couched in the contemptuous tone the *Epitaph* always used about Johnson: "Mr. George Johnson who, well-armed, watches over the Bisbee diligence's stores of cart grease."

There was Johnson, middle-aged, thin and a laughing-stock, dreaming his unfortunate boyish dreams of being one of the great ones of the West—while his wife cooked his meals and his children played round him without his bothering about them.

His thoughts were in the West.

One evening in October the *Epitaph* came out with a special number, just the one thin sheet which the editor had obviously sent a boy to Crystal Palace to sell.

It contained a confused report of the diligence from Bisbee having been attacked. According to its account a woman had come riding into the town on one of the diligence horses and told how she and her husband—his name was M. G. Kellog and he apparently was an ironmonger and banker renowned for sobriety, who used to give money to the miners' children when he met them on the street—had been the only passengers in the diligence which was on its way to Tombstone. A mile outside the city, just as it was growing dark, a man with a handkerchief over his face had ridden up to the horses and fired a shot. She had not noticed him shoot at the coach, but she felt how her husband beside her had collapsed. She also heard the coachman say in an amazed voice:

"What the devil now, we haven't any money with us!"

She had shaken her husband and called to him, then she had felt his heart and realizing that he was dead, had uttered a scream of horror, just as the bandit rode up to the passengers' seat, pistol in hand. At the sound the bandit's horse had reared, and he had fallen off. She didn't bother about him, but just clasped her dead husband; but the coachman, however, saw that the bandit had dropped his revolver and jumped down to grapple with him. The bandit got to his feet and ran; his horse bolted. The coachman unharnessed one of the diligence horses for Mrs. Kellogg and asked her to ride to the town for help to get her dead husband home and for a few men to help hunt the murderer who certainly could not get very far on foot.

So much was in that extra number of the *Epitaph*.

The ordinary issue which followed later told the rest of the story.

The usual procedure in cases of attack on the diligence was set in motion—the sheriff got a posse together, the undertaker harnessed up his waggon, and they all rode off with a crowd of the curious following in their wake. When they reached the unharnessed diligence everybody stood round in a respectful ring while the undertaker and his assistant went inside to lift Mr. Kellogg out. They stayed inside so long that it made people wonder, and finally the sheriff cautiously stepped forward and enquired what was the matter.

The tall undertaker then stepped out and said:

"Mr. Kellogg has not been shot. There's no wound on him. He died of heart failure."

Everybody stood silent. It could not make much difference to Mrs. Kellog how her husband had died, but the sheriff, said *Epitaph*'s reporter, walked away and sat down on a stone and lit a cigar and relapsed into what undoubtedly was profound meditation.

After a while he stood up and said:

"That alters matters. We must get hold of the bandit, that's obvious, since he's made himself guilty of attempted robbery with violence. But as a hold-up this is the most miserable attempt I've seen, and we can't accuse him of murder nor of robbery with violence, scarcely of assault. Mr. Kellogg died of heart failure caused by fright and nothing has been stolen. Damn me, if this isn't the queerest thing I've seen for months."

The sheriff then rode off with his posse to follow the trail of the coachman who, with the cuteness of the West, had torn bits first off his handkerchief and then off his shirt and thrown them into the bushes as he rode after the bandit.

After some hours it was obvious that the trail was leading back to Tombstone in a wide arc, and the posse set off at a gallop for the town. From a distance, even before they saw the first weather-cocks on the mine-towers, the sheriff and his men realized that the town was in turmoil. Something must have happened. There was a big crowd outside the Circuit Court and when the sheriff got a bit closer and shaded his eyes with his hand, he reined in so abruptly that he nearly fell off his horse.

There was a man hanging from the big telegraph pole.

The sheriff put on a spurt and rode into the crowd kicking people right and left and shouting to clear the way, and asked:

"What the devil have you done, you calamities? Who have you hanged?"

And they shouted back in chorus:

"We've hanged that damned George Johnson who murdered old Mr. Kellogg tonight."

Now *Epitaph*'s reporter had gone with the sheriff in the other-wise correct, but in this case mistaken, view that that would be where things would happen. However, the paper had pieced together from the reports of eye witnesses an account of what had happened in Tombstone while the posse, the reporter and the curious were away.

An hour or so after they had gone, the coachman had come jogging in on a heavy diligence horse leading behind him on a trace George Johnson who was smiling arrogantly and holding himself very erect and looking serious and solemn and above all fearfully high and mighty.

"Here's the swine who shot old Mr. Kellogg," said the coach-man, "and I suggest that we save the sheriff a lot of unnecessary work."

There was a tremendous commotion in the town. Suddenly it became a point of honour to have the murderer hanged before the sheriff got back, so that they could show him how efficient the citizens of Tombstone could be on their own initiative. The only possible fly in the ointment was the fact that the murderer himself just looked delighted, and the general feeling was that it was a very hardened brute they had had in their midst without realizing how evil he was. Johnson's wife came and wept, but he just looked at her and said:

"Be calm, Nancy, I knew that this would come one day. I

131

could not go on like that without getting caught in the end."

He was unnaturally unconcerned and proud when they placed the noose round his neck and set him up on a horse. The *Epitaph* was sensible enough not to mention the names of those who organized the lynching. "A gentleman," it said, "adroitly threw the rope over the telegraph pole." Then they asked George Johnson if he had anything to say.

"I have had my due share of life," he said. "I chose to live on the wrong side of the law, but I do not regret it. I am sorry for those I have shot, and I imagine I shall be meeting a good few of them soon. I request a Christian burial."

Somebody gave the horse a smack, it bolted and left George Johnson hanging in the air.

When the sheriff explained to those who had done the lynching that George Johnson had not shot anybody nor stolen a brass farthing, but merely fallen off his horse when a woman screamed, gloom fell upon everybody. In silence they organized a collection for Mrs. Johnson which brought her over 800 dollars, more money than she had ever had in her life.

A poker-player is quoted as having said in Crystal Palace that evening:

"However disagreeable the whole affair has been, no one could have been happier at what transpired than Mr. George Johnson."

The *Epitaph* just calls the man "a gambler", but he must have been the only psychologist in Tombstone then. He understood that George Johnson had achieved the object of his dreams when for one hour the whole town thought him a dangerous desperado.

That, I realized as I closed the old files, was the explanation of the two strangest inscriptions at Boot Hill:

M. E. KELLOGG—1882
DIED A NATURAL DEATH

and

GEORGE JOHNSON
HANGED BY MISTAKE

15

PREPARATIONS

While Margareta was at Mary Lou's helping her and Ysabel make crinolines for the Helldorado, I drove aimlessly about the prairie in the Professor's 1922 model, or else I lounged in the back seat of an old crock in Chisholm's workshop, where it began to dawn on me that, if the tension was not eased soon, Tombstone would become a sort of cage in which Chisholm would be incarcerated as cruelly as the mountain cats the old man with the torn hands kept in the cages behind Hassayamper's hacienda.

My field of vision was bounded by the Dragon Mountains and Huachucas, and by the hard, glaring cover of the sunlight. The town breathed quietly in the heat, like a kitten under the unintentionally cruel hand of a playful child which lies quite still to prevent anything happening and hopes that it will soon be able to jump up and play again.

Chisholm lay on his trolley under one or other of the cars swearing softly to himself, for business was too good and he never had time for what he wanted to do. At intervals he would take hold of the step of the car he happened to be under and pull himself half way out for a chat.

"Darned hard that Ysabel never goes away."

"Couldn't you stand her a trip to Tucson?"

"That'd look too obvious. I send her in to Tucson, and then in the evening I go to Mary Lou's. It wouldn't do."

"But Margareta and I could take her in for a few days."

"That wouldn't do either. It would seem such a put-up business. You hang about here every afternoon, so everyone would realize that it was something we had schemed."

He lay gazing up at the roof for a moment, then he took hold of the step and pulled himself in under the car again.

I went and bought some cigars and returned to my old files, where I blew cigar smoke through a cloud of the dust of fifty years. I sat there aimlessly turning the pages and trying to devise ways and means how affection might triumph in Tombstone.

April 29, 1878.

"Milton, most glorious of English poets, wrote: 'Hail, Love, true source. . . .' and by that he meant the true grounds for all earthly happiness. For when hands meet and hearts are inclined towards each other, when two people link their futures, it involves combining all that is bitter and sweet in life, all that has any significance. The truth of these reflexions stood forth clearly yesterday afternoon, when Mr. Edward Warren Perkins of the Convention Mines and Miss Angel Annabelle Howe were joined in matrimony by Rev. G. L. Pearson. Spirits were of the best after the ceremony, despite the fact that Joe from Baltimore, specially engaged for the occasion, contrived to set off his fireworks too early and so unfortunately as to inflict slight burns upon the bride's father. The evening concluded, however, in the best concord."

I looked up towards the mountains away across the prairie, at the steeples of the episcopal church and baptist chapel, and at the white adobe houses lying cowering beneath the desolation. There was Chisholm pining and Mary Lou yearning for affection and dreaming of the great security over and above that of her silver and Lazy M and of the haciendas that would be hers, and of Crystal Palace: that long bar was to be hers too.

From many quarters we were hearing about Mary Lou's former husband and what sort of a person he had been.

Hassayamper said:

"I take it that he wasn't so dumb. I don't want to talk about it, but I believe he wasn't so dumb."

Titus:

"A lonely chap. He dreamed of being popular, the town's genial host, but he was so jealous of his dignity that no one dared be with him. Do you know what I think? He was European. We Americans aren't dignified as such. Oh, yes, we stick to our flag and we'll allow no devil to say that we have worse water pipes or drainage systems than any other country, or that we are less democratic. But look at Tombstone here: is there anyone here who lives for his prestige? What do you Europeans do but go about with your hands sweaty from holding on to your prestige? Mary Lou's fellow was European. His prestige was his religion. I don't understand how he ever landed here."

Chuck:

134

"Well. . . ."

He sent a squirt of saliva mixed with tobacco juice on to the dust in front of the drug store, before going on:

"Well. He had queer eyes and a queer mouth. He always pursed his mouth as though someone had just been insolent to him or as if he expected someone were going to be. And his eyes were never still. Sometimes we would go to Phoenix on the razzle; he would stand treat and be lavish; and the moment he caught sight of a policeman, he couldn't rest till he was sure the policeman wanted to have him, if not shoot him. Then he was satisfied, for then his pride was hurt. He wanted it to be hurt, that was life to him. At times, too, he had his mouth half open, and then he was expecting to be insulted or passed over or something. But he was good at everything he undertook. Though not to the extent . . . not like Chisholm, I mean, it goes without saying that Chisholm will manage whatever it is. Mary Lou's old chap went at things as though he would burst. Sometimes if you had done something well, I mean if I had ridden in a rodeo or broken a horse or something like that . . . he always came and praised you, which I thought was decent till I discovered the reason why he did it. Every time he had praised you, his mouth would be left half-open and his eyes would stray, and then he would say: 'I imagine that in this devilish jealous town nobody else has given you a pat on the back. . . .' And do you know why he said that? Well, he looked at you so anxiously because he was mortally afraid someone else might have praised you, and he wanted you to say: 'No, of course not.' And that's what I did say in the end, even if it was the other way round, for I saw how grieved he became otherwise. So I always said: 'No, what the hell do you think?' And then he heaved a sigh of relief. No one was to be praised behind his back. . . . No, he was a darned disaster."

The Professor:

"When we had people to dinner he always sat with the ladies telling them how fast he had driven, or how he had rung some-one up and done a good deal. He lived in the hope of playing the lead in a masculine world. Do you understand? He wanted to know all the tricks and to be able to do all the things men do. He could not tell you how he had bought petrol on the road without somehow making out that he had been the devil of a fellow and how well he had managed. And all the while his eyes were on you begging for you to realize what a wonderful person he was. When any big bug came to the town, he would just stand beside him and laugh and all but die of happiness at being one of a lot of fine fellows and stand and chat. . . . He never cared about Mary Lou. Other than that she was smart and stylish. He could not even manage to be jealous; he did not know what that was, for he was not in love. He could not be. I've heard, too, that he did not take any notice of Ysabel, when they had her. I was not here then. It took him all his time just being manly."

Slattery:

"Him? I've some inside dope on him." Then a lengthy laugh. "He wanted to be a ladykiller. I know from Phoenix—between ourselves I know a madam there—that he used to drive in and go to the brothel they had there until last year and laugh and tell them what a speed he had got out of his old bus coming there. But he would never be alone with a girl. He would go first to the Lion or the Elks or some other club to find a chap to go with him. He always wanted another couple in the room. And afterwards, when it was all over, he ran off as soon as he could and dragged his companion to a lot of bars, where he would go and whisper to everyone telling them what they had been up to. He lay with women merely so as to be able to tell people about it afterwards. He was a swine. A little frightened swine. . . ."

Slattery laughed again, not a long and hearty laugh this time, but resignedly, as though in the midst of his jocularity he had unexpectedly begun to think about all the mean and pitiable things he knew of. After a while the laugh became his old one, and when he had recovered his breath, he told us an involved story of how Mary Lou's husband had been taken ill in Crystal Palace while trying to show people how they ought to drink.

Those were the opinions of Mary Lou's former husband given us without our asking. He had married again somewhere, and no doubt felt a little sense of triumph at being married for the second time and having one woman behind him. Someone had seen him in Denver the previous year, sitting with beseeching eyes telling people how fast he had driven there in his car.

Judah never said anything. Nor did Mary Lou.

The days passed in a sort of slight exaltation. All the men were letting their beards grow, and I felt dirty and raspy because of it. It was scarcely made any better by my having to lie down every now and again because my nose was bleeding. Chuck and I went up to some old attic in search of clothes, and I was lucky enough to find some fairly reasonable boots that I could manage to walk in. Then I got hold of a revolver and taught myself to load it with blank cartridges, and then, without thinking what I was doing, I found myself practising what Wyatt Earp had been so expert at: drawing it—getting the revolver up out of its holster as swiftly as possible.

That business of Mary Lou and Chisholm was now weighing upon us, and, discussing it in our room in the evenings, we agreed that the small town was the worst social unit, whether it was filled with shops selling picture postcards or long bars.

We were now all beginning to look like savages. Hockstaedt, the marshal, was the fattest man in Tombstone; he was a peculiar shape with a long pot-belly and long, narrow legs, and it was almost unsavoury to see him pacing along Allen Street with long pig bristles all over his face. In Crystal Palace Judah had screened off the little stage with the piano, and there the High School girls rehearsed the can-can. Hockstaedt was allowed in behind the screens and he played the piano, and sometimes we joined in from our side and sang with them, and we were all very eager to see the dress rehearsal.

The Professor went about everywhere with a mass of paper under his arm, and he turned his hairdressing saloon into the headquarters of the Helldorado. No sooner had he finished with a customer than he would come out in his sombrero and short-sleeved hairdresser's coat and dash off somewhere in his 1927. There had already been letters from the picture magazines and the big Sunday supplements in the East wanting to come and photograph it, and the news films had rung up and booked rooms at Oleander's. Our impatience increased.

The first tourist to arrive was an incredibly excited man and his family from Weehawken, New Jersey. I thought that sounded Indian and imagined that it must lie somewhere up by the great lakes in Cooper's country, till I looked at the map and discovered that it was opposite Manhattan and had two ferries an hour to it, and that I had even been there one rainy evening when I had wanted a trip across the Hudson to see the lights; before that I had been in a Catholic church to be out of the rain and then in a bad variety. The town was wrongly named: Weehawken, that sounded redolent of Dutch and Indian memories, but it was merely a heap of bricks with the thundering Pulaski highway crossing it.

This man from Weehawken was beside himself with excitement. He had come just for the Helldorado, and it was his first holiday for three years. His Chevrolet had kept going the whole way and he had his wife and two children with him, a girl and a boy under ten. He went about with his camera day after day systematically taking photographs, and presumably in the end he must have photographed every street corner and the name-board of every shop, and probably could have supplied a picture of every inhabitant of Tombstone. He was so busy with all this, that it was a day or two before he had time to begin talking with people. He was a commercial traveller. For some reason or other his wife never went out. She sat inside sewing.

The first time the commercial traveller came to spend the evening properly at Crystal Palace, having calmed down with his photography and grown accustomed to being in Tombstone, he was very friendly to me because Sweden had not been in the war. I tried to change the subject, but he insisted on lauding Sweden and me for what we had not done.

"What could you have done in the war? We did not go in till we were attacked, and that was that damned Roosevelt's own fault. You were sensible to stay out."

That was the first time anyone had said a word about the war, and I had almost forgotten it. The war they talked about there was the Civil War. I had no idea what the people in Tombstone had done in the war. It had never occurred to me to wonder where they had been between 1942 and 1945.

The commercial traveller did not know what he was doing. He stirred up a storm that had laid buried and smouldering under the floor tiles of Crystal Palace. Titus paled. He was anti-Roosevelt, but he did not like the commercial traveller—he had said so the first day—for the man had thought him a Jew and not a Greek, and also, he was a prominent member of Weehawken's invisible anti-semitic association. The Professor's face also paled, for he was a supporter of Roosevelt. It was the same with Roosevelt as with Wyatt Earp. People behaved as though he might come round the corner at any moment. He was not dead. He was everywhere around us. People like the commercial traveller resurrected him once a day and kicked him about, and the Professor spoke with his tongue. There began a thoroughly confused discussion in which Titus tried not to associate himself with the commercial traveller at the same time as agreeing with him, and the Professor squashed him to Titus' great delight. It was quite chaotic.

"Oh, Roosevelt and his old woman," exclaimed Titus. "There isn't a damned student comes to this country, no Indian who has never been in India and is studying mass psychology or social biology or whatever nonsense it is at London University on his father's diamonds, who can't go and talk poppycock with Mrs. Roosevelt. She and her world, and we must all stick together, must we—what damned nonsense! nothing but a horde of semi-idiot Japs and Indians that squat round her on the grass and hatch out a lot of rotten nonsense. Roosevelt wasn't as stupid as all that, but he was not far behind her where that's concerned."

The Professor went through the New Deal and the social reforms while Titus nodded or shook his head and the commercial traveller snorted, and although the atmosphere was slowly but surely becoming thoroughly unpleasant, I was surprised to find myself thinking that it was nice to find these signs of normal life and normal squabbles.

The commercial traveller, however, was no asset in our society; even Titus who shared his views, realized that. He was stupid and bad and vulgar and boasted that he was a churchwarden in his congregation in Weehawken and said that Jews were worse behaved than negroes, and he kept on like that for three or four evenings before they began to give him the cold shoulder. He came as a stupid reminder of the world in the east, the world without romance and childishness and games, where a Helldorado was something akin to a students' rag and not a playful manifestation in all seriousness: a vulgar, shabby and industrious world where everybody worked like slaves and never looked up at the outline of the hills or thoughtfully picked up a nail or some sheep droppings from the ground.

Sadly I began to wonder when we would have to leave Tombstone and return to reality.

16

THE RESCUE

We were in our room talking about Menander's invalid wife and mending an old rucksack, when through the window we saw Chuck dash past in his little van and take the corner by the school as though on an errand of life and death. We stood up and looked, but could see nothing but the cloud of his dust still hanging over the rose bushes in front of the *Epitaph*.

Ten minutes later someone came running towards our courtyard. It was the Professor. He was red in the face and recklessly jumping the cacti to get to us quicker. He waved to us, but when he did reach our veranda, his breath had deserted him and he could scarcely speak.

"It's the commercial traveller's kids," he panted. "They must have gone down the mine. They've been gone since this morning and no one's seen them round the mines."

It was Saturday afternoon and most people had gone in to Tucson to the cinema.

I had no conception of what ought to be done, but had a vague idea that as many of us as possible would be needed to haul on ropes and lower each other down shafts and run about the galleries with balls of string. We put on our oldest clothes and ran after the Professor, while Menander pacified his wife and came shambling after us.

The openings into the mines lay on the far side of the rusty railway tracks west of the town, beyond the Birdcage Theatre and the old County Court. There were some old tip-waggons on a couple of narrow gauge tracks and the boy and girl had been seen pushing them to and fro that morning and also clambering about some old pumping apparatus. The commercial traveller had been out photographing desert flowers, and the mother had been sitting indoors mending the children's clothes.

Nobody had seen the children since half past ten. Their father had gone to look for them at about two o'clock. They were nowhere to be found. The Professor had gone to the top of the church tower with his glasses and twice scrutinized the plain stone by stone: they had vanished.

The mine was the only possibility. This was Toughnut, Schieffelin's first big find.

It was when they realized this that they had sent for Chuck, that being the obvious thing to do. Nobody knew if anyone then living in Tombstone had ever been down the mines, but it was assumed that if anybody could do anything, it would be Chuck.

I myself had never been right up to Toughnut. There was a ricketty fence round the entrance, the ground round the black hole looked unsafe and there was nothing to see. The commercial traveller and Chuck had stood there for some minutes calling down into the darkness without receiving an answer. The Professor's wife had gone to be with the sewing mother who still remained invisible. The atmosphere was ghastly; the dazzling sunlight, the father trying to appear calm as he stood leaned forward with his hands on his knees, an attitude which he reckoned would let him appear unconstrained, while despair tugged at him.

"Ah, you know what kids are," said the Professor and gave him a slap on the shoulder. "They never hurt themselves."

But the hole looked very black.

One could not yet be quite sure that the children were down in the mine. Chuck padded round the mouth stepping cautiously and gazing down at the ground. Occasionally a stone detached itself from under his weight and went rattling down. The sound lost itself deep, deep below. Chisholm came running from his garage with a wealth of lasso looped over one arm. There was not a sign of anyone else. Behind us the town was as still and quiet as death.

There were five of us men and Margareta: the father, Chuck, the Professor, Chisholm and I. There was a brief, empty, terrifying moment while we all straightened up, and I was convinced that no one knew what to do next. There was a surge of hopelessness, and the Professor said before he had time to stop himself and prevent the father hearing:

"There are miles and miles of galleries down there."

Chuck came back from circling the opening and said:

"The two are down there all right."

"How do you know?" asked the commercial traveller.

"They have left a distinct track by the edge," Chuck replied and pointed at it. "It looks impossible, but it isn't so difficult for a couple of small kids to get down there. Look. They have held on to those stones that stick out. It's been like climbing down a tree."

"They may have tumbled straight down," said the commercial traveller, deathly pale.

"Not necessarily," Chuck said quickly and in an ordinary, matter-of-fact tone of voice, that finally broke the spell of fright and anxiety that lay over us and made me feel suddenly energetic and calm and full of ideas how we should get hold of the children.

Chisholm fastened a stone to one end of his lasso and threw it into the hole. We heard it strike against the wall before the line went taut.

"Now we'll see," said Chisholm. "I have torches here, three of them. We're assuming that they are straight down in the hole and have not crawled into the galleries. If they've done that, it'll be trickier. We'd need some map or sketch of the mine then. There's said to be one at the old County Court. But if Chuck goes down now and they haven't crept into any of the galleries, we'll have them up in five minutes."

"Let's go," said Chuck.

Chisholm passed the lasso over and under a rail of the track beside the pump, and Chuck took a turn with the other end round his body and with astounding nonchalance plunged into the blackness of the mine. His left hand holding the rope above him and his right holding himself off. We saw his big hat disappear on the side where he had said he had found the tracks. Chisholm had braced one heel against a sleeper and stood tensed like a Volga boatman, supporting Chuck's weight.

We waited some minutes.

Then Chuck called from down below.

The Professor bent forward:

"Are they there?"

"Nope," called Chuck.

"Can you see the bottom?" the Professor shouted.

"There's a good bit left, but I can see down to the shelf," Chuck shouted. His voice sounded as though it came from an empty swimming bath, echoing round and round before it reached up to us.

Then his voice came again:

"There's a shelf down here, and then another hole leading straight down."

Up above, we stood silent, thinking this over.

"Good God," said the commercial traveller, "they can have crawled in anywhere and got lost in the galleries."

Then Chisholm said:

"At all events they haven't fallen while climbing down the wall. They're alive."

And he gave me a look behind the father's back, as much as to say that that was more than he could ever hope.

Chisholm now assumed command on the surface:

"Professor, take Chuck's van and try to get hold of a plan of this damned Toughnut mine. Chuck will have to get down to that shelf, and then you, Swede, must climb down and help him. I'll go down too, so you'll have to handle the rope up here," he said with a peremptory look at the commercial traveller.

Everybody accepted Chisholm's orders. Margareta went with the Professor as he dived for Chuck's van, and they disappeared in a cloud of dust. Chisholm shouted down to Chuck that he should try and climb down to the shelf, and that he and I were going to come. Chisholm gave me a torch which I stuffed inside my shirt. From where we stood sorting ropes we could see the town; the air was strangely still and clear, and it looked dead and abandoned. It was, in fact, an open question how many people there might be in it. Judah and Mary Lou had driven to Tucson to see to some documents, Hassayamper sat closeted with his Apache queen; Hockstaedt was in Bisbee.

Away in the distance we saw the van stop by the old County Court and Margareta and the Professor get out and run round trying the doors and windows. Then we saw the Professor at the back door raise his foot and just kick it in: the sight of that had the same effect as Chuck's voice when he told us that the children need not necessarily have killed themselves—it freed us from a sort of oppression. It occurred to me that when in a desperate situation, if you did something definite every five minutes, it would relieve your feeling of fear and keep you going.

A minute or two later I was on my way down the hole with Chisholm and the commercial traveller holding on up above. I had made a loop of rope around me, as I had seen Chuck do, but I was not half as quick in my movements as he. I could tell from my breathing how nervous I really was: I found myself hysterically breathing out some silly tune instead of taking things calmly. At one point, after kicking myself away from the side to avoid bumping on it, I swung so violently that I touched the other face and Chisholm shouted down asking what I was up to.

I was not particularly afraid yet; there was something understandably exciting about hanging swaying there. As I made my way down, my idea of the string occurred to me again. I would never have thought of it, if I had not had such a lively recollection of Tom Sawyer's adventure in the cave. I could scarcely wait to get down to Chuck to suggest it.

We were standing on quite a big platform. Ten paces to the left, away from the town, in the direction of Lucky Cuss mine, was the opening of another wide hole that led obliquely downwards. Looking up, I could see a round bit of sky sixty-five feet above and the silhouette of the commercial traveller.

"We can't see anything yet," I called up to him.

For the next five minutes Chuck and I had nothing to do but wait for Chisholm. We were anxious whether the lasso would hold him and how he would manage the last fifteen feet when you had to jump. Chuck listened to my suggestion about the string, but said very placidly:

"That won't be needed, if one person only searches. I won't get lost. If you stay here, I'll go into the holes, and I know exactly where I'm going, so I can always find my way back. The kids must be together. I'll bring back the one who is more afraid, then you send her or him up, while I go for the other."

It sounded simple. And to emphasize how simple it all was, Chuck produced tobacco and cigarette papers from his breast pocket and rolled himself a cigarette.

"But they could be miles inside the mountain," I hazarded after a while. "The Professor said that Toughnut and Lucky Cuss are supposed to link up somewhere deep down."

"That's correct," said Chuck drily. "But there's water in the galleries. That's why they aren't worked any longer. There's masses of silver left. But a good fifty people have ruined themselves trying to pump the mines dry—it won't pay to start working them again. It was the water that broke Tombstone.

144

Twenty thousand people in the town one day and a mass flight from it the next. I don't know when the water came. Just a year or so after Wyatt left. It came first in Toughnut here, nearest the town. Then, only a few weeks afterwards, both Lucky Cuss and Contention were flooded. A lot of idiots thought the water would be the town's salvation; it would solve Tombstone's water problem, water having till then been the most difficult thing of all. People had drilled a few baby wells here and there, but for the first few years water cost a lot, more than beer. I believe there was a leader in the *Epitaph* saying that that was the end of San Francisco, now Tombstone would be the greatest city in the West. We had all that 'Frisco had, oysters and champagne, and now damn it, we had water as well. But twenty or thirty miners were drowned in the galleries, and they had taken all the silver there was from the shafts that were not flooded. The silver that is left all lies deeper. I have heard it said that it would cost more to pump out the water than what could be got from the silver in ten years. Anyway silver is supposed to be just dirt these days. Today it has to be stuff they can make bombs out of."

While Chuck was giving me this lightning sketch of Tombstone's economic development, the heavy-weight Chisholm had begun to ease himself down and I could glimpse Margareta and the Professor in the little round opening far above us. They had been away only a quarter of an hour.

"I found the big plan," shouted the Professor. "It was on the wall. We didn't see it at first."

"I don't think we'll need it," muttered Chuck. "They can't have gone far in."

Then he lowered his voice:

"I'll tell you why. I've been down here once for fun. Fifty yards or so on down that black hole there's a skeleton which looks a bit grim, for there are bits of clothing left on it. I don't think the kids would have dared go past. The worst would be, if they had got such a fright that they had run off headlong without thinking what they were doing. But even then they must have come across water pretty soon. They can't possibly be far away."

"Couldn't gases have killed them? Or they have drowned?"

"I don't know."

Now Chisholm was hanging above us, large and heavy,

blocking our view of the sky. All at once a phrase came into my mind, I do not know where from: "Life's forces in alliance to maintain life." What was it? A strange, blissful sense of happiness came over me when I saw Chisholm, clumsily, hesitantly searching for a foothold and looking down between his legs before taking the last jump, and I remembered how I had felt the first time up on Boot Hill, how you got a direct feel of people: the widower Chisholm, the garage proprietor who was almost never cheerful. The mysterious cowboy-cum-plumber Chuck, who smoked cigarettes he rolled himself and to whom nothing was frightening or strange, who was as much at home with the darkness down here as with broken-off cactus branches, dropped nuts and bits of sheep droppings. And I myself.

Chisholm thudded down.

"I think the rock has held," he remarked.

There was a large protruding roll of paper stuffed inside his jacket, which was fastened with a zip-fastener, and this he at once produced and shone his torch on it.

"Can you see which way up it goes?" he said.

The plan was about eight feet square. We spread it on the uneven rock floor. It was easy to understand, but also shattering. We could clearly see the point where we were and how from it a confusion of galleries led in all directions, upwards and downwards and to the sides; it was pretty evident that we might have to spend days down there.

Chuck repeated his theory of the skeleton and the water. With his finger he traced the course of the big hole below us and indicated the place where the water was. His skeleton should be somewhere near the water line. Just before that there were five galleries branching off.

"Shall we search a gallery each, in turn?" I asked not without apprehension.

"I think you're too big for the galleries," said Chuck. "The children could get into them, and I can probably crawl in or worm in. You would stick. At all events you would not be able to turn. They had some galleries that were just communication passages, through which the little Mexicans scuttled, for they could crawl in them."

The purport of this was that only Chuck could go into the galleries, and that we two must wait outside. We would be needed when the children had to be got out of the hole and up to the surface.

"They can't have gone into any of the galleries on the way down," Chuck decided. "They would never have managed to climb in. So we must go down. If we look, perhaps we'll come across some tracks."

I really did look, but I was unable to find any. I shone my torch on every bit of rock as we stepped down the steeply sloping gallery. After only ten or twelve yards it became so steep that it was no longer possible to walk or hold a torch. First I sat down and went along with my back to the rock as though I were on a ladder; then I had to turn and climb down. I went last, Chuck first. Sometimes in my hurry I put my foot on Chisholm's head or shoulders.

Afterwards, I found that I had no idea how deep down we had climbed or how long we had been at it. I thought of nothing; I had no other concern but to stick down a foot, grope, find a foothold, let the other foot pass it, lower my hands—all in utter darkness, for there was neither room in my hands for my torch nor time to use it. I had put it back inside my shirt.

None of us spoke. Chisholm was breathing very heavily. He it was who said that we should not call to the children, as that would merely confuse them, and then they might start running or crawling towards the sound of our voices and perish while pursuing a treacherous echo. I felt squashed by his cool dispassionateness.

It felt as though we had been climbing down all day, when I heard Chuck say:

"All right, here's granddad."

He had found the skeleton.

I stopped where I was with my feet on two jutting stones, and for a while did not venture down. Strangely enough it was the remains of clothing that scared me. If it had just been a skeleton possibly it would not have worried me; but the thought of an old pair of trousers took me by the throat. I could not help asking Chuck where it was and so revealed my reluctance to find myself sitting beside it.

"Where are you?" Chuck said, and at that moment I felt myself kick someone on the head.

"That's me at all events," said Chuck. "Keep to the left and you won't land on the old boy."

I got down on to a small shelf. Across it lay a mouldered beam that felt cold and damp. It had a broken end jutting over a hole. I knew from the plan that this was where the mine proper began. If I missed my footing here, I would drop straight into the bowels of the earth and disappear into a great pool of fusty water to join thirty old miners from the days of Tombstone's greatness. I leaned very slightly over the hole and pretended to look down, but for all I saw I might as well have had my eyes tight shut. Chuck and Chisholm were muttering behind me. They had switched on their torches and were looking round the walls. You could stand upright there, leaning against the face down which we had come. A narrow rail ran round the opening, and there were iron clamps in the walls. Chuck explained that the beam was the remains of a hoist, and on the way down he had come across bits of old rail up which the loads of silver had been hauled with a winch.

"They weren't so backward," he said. "They had things really well arranged here."

In the jerky light of the torches I now saw the skeleton. It was doubled up as I remembered seeing in pictures of the Indians' method of burial; the hands lay slightly in front of the feet, the head hung between the knees and was entirely covered by a mouldy black hat. There was no trace of trousers, but the remains of the sleeves of a jacket still covered the arms. One look was enough to satisfy me. That skeleton was no more than a curiosity, and afterwards, when I was back in the sunlight up above, it struck me that I had never even wondered who it was with whom I had spent that half hour down there. It was almost a disappointment to find myself so little interested, and I felt slightly disturbed that I had been so unreceptive to the experience.

What did interest me were the five galleries leading into the bowels of the mountain. The very openings looked more awful than the skeleton, like scrofulous wounds, suppurating, flaking little orifices in something half decayed. They were roughly on a level with our knees. Three could be reached without difficulty from our shelf, but two were in the opposite wall and to reach them you had to climb out over the hole using the iron clamps.

It seemed to me that we would not need to worry about them: the children could not possibly have got across.

There on that shelf I again fell prey to that agitation that had laid hold of me up above, before I became busy lowering myself on the rope and then climbing down. I was afraid now, filled with a creepy fear of never being able to get out of the darkness, of spending hours groping with my hands about the walls and finally vanishing into some hole. I felt that, even when I was in the company of two adult men. How could the children have stood it? For a moment there seemed no other possibility than that they had climbed down the same steep face as we had, and then, when they reached the shelf, just fallen into the hole and vanished.

"Could we ever find them if they had tumbled in here?" I asked.

Chuck and Chisholm were standing with the beams of their torches fixed on one of the openings.

"We don't need to search that," said Chuck after a while. "If they've fallen in there, they'll have died at once. We'll stick to these holes. I'll go in now, only I don't know where to begin."

I peered down into the big hole and tried to imagine what the children would have done when they came to the shelf; I could find no support for the idea that they would have climbed inside that dark wall. We did not know whether they had had candles or matches with them, but they certainly had not had a torch. I was convinced now that they had just slipped from the slope down into the hole and the water.

Chisholm and Chuck made their preparations with calm, unmoved expressions on their faces. Chuck had lit another cigarette and the glow from it spread across his chin as he inhaled. Chisholm even hummed now and again.

"Well, if I was a kid," said Chisholm, "I would take the easiest hole to climb into, the one most convenient to get at. . . ."

He expanded the idea, while Chuck smoked in silence. When Chisholm had finished and pointed out the gallery with which he thought Chuck ought to begin, the latter said:

"If I was a youngster and had slid down into this hole and had enough courage left to play, then obviously I would go for the worst hole."

And without waiting for our views, he balanced along the rail over the deep hole, holding on to the iron clamps. We watched in silence, and when he came in front of the gallery of his choice, we directed our torches straight at the opening. Chuck groped for a handhold inside; then he bent his knees, and with one hand inside the gallery and the other clutching an iron clamp he pulled himself up into the opening and lay there on his stomach.

At that instant the clamp he was grasping with his left hand came away. But nothing happened, for he was already balanced in the gallery. Neither Chisholm nor he did anything to show that they realized he had very nearly been killed.

We saw him worm his way into the gallery till only the soles of his boots were visible. Then they and he disappeared. I had imagined that he would stick his head out and say something, for as far as we knew we might never see him again. Then the simple explanation struck me: the gallery was too narrow for him to turn round. Again the hopelessness of our whole rescue expedition struck me.

Chisholm and I had nothing to do, so we sat down. I sat on the rotten beam with my back to the skeleton, and Chisholm sat on the edge of the hole with his feet dangling over the depths. At first he was so silent that I took fright and switched on my torch to see if he was still there.

He looked gravely at the beam, then he gave a little laugh and said:

"Tomorrow Mary Lou and I are going to get married."

I switched off my torch and said into the darkness:

"Congratulations. All the best to you."

"Thanks."

After a pause he filled in the details.

"We're driving to the justice of the peace in Bisbee after Church. We're only taking Ysabel with us. We'll tell Judah and Hassayamper afterwards."

"Do you think they'll have anything against it?"

"Against it? I'm the best match in the town," said Chisholm, quite naturally, as though that were obvious. "They've been fishing to get me for ages. It was just that I didn't want to hang up my hat, but Mary Lou's got me away from that idea now. That's been the whole trouble. Apart from this damned town, of course, and Lazy M and all the ideas people have. I shall sell the garage and the sites I have in the town here and buy out the Professor and Titus and the whole Lazy M gang, and then you'll see what cattle rearing's like. It's all nonsense about the ranch being turned into a pension. That's Titus' idea. He wants to make some quick money, and then he'll get out. Slattery and Chuck can run it, and I'll have highballs ready for them and keep guard on the cash box and smoke cigars. You know that I'm Indian? Indian and Scots. Now I shall be owning our own land again. I shall employ an old Indian to serve coffee and have a Highlander in a kilt to play the bagpipes after dinner. . . ."

He laughed softly and long, then relapsed into silence.

After a while he said:

"But if we don't find the kids, we won't very well be able to go and get married tomorrow."

I thought how utterly wrong my angle of the romance between Chisholm and Mary Lou had been, but I comforted myself a little by telling myself that after achieving his long desired triumph he was fibbing a bit to me and that he really was in love with her, enough anyway: with the girlish way she swung her arms and her provocative hint of unattainability Mary Lou was easy to fall in love with.

Then the tips of the fingers of my left hand happened to touch what presumably were bits of wood off the beam, but which could also have been the skeleton's fingers, and that set me thinking about Chuck inside the gallery there.

"Why does one never see Mrs. Chuck?" I asked Chisholm.

"She's paralysed," Chisholm replied at once. "But you can perfectly well meet her. Chuck is glad if anyone asks, though he'll never come and tell you about it of his own accord. Before there had been some chance for her, but now they must have given up hope and Chuck can't talk about how she is. Everybody used to ask him before. She was paralysed when he came here and sent for her. Now people think that it's better if he isn't asked about it. She's English. Chuck brought her back with him after the war. She was in a bar in Belfast playing backgammon when they met, and she was all alone and Chuck married her after a couple of days. Just before the Normandy invasion."

There was another long pause:

"Strange chap, Chuck, isn't he?" said Chisholm. "A paralysed wife. He mends everything, shoes horses. Looks after the old diligence. Unstops all the blocked drains. Rescues children in mines."

"That we don't know yet."

"Yes, damn it, we do. If Chuck says the kids went into that gallery, then they did. He'll come out with them."

"How's he off for money?"

"Enough."

"Enough to manage?"

"No, enough to be all right. Plumbing's no bad job in Arizona. He has money in the bank. Two good ground plots."

I laughed.

"What's funny about that?"

"No, it's not that. I can't explain. It's so stupid. I suppose I've read too much about Wyatt Earp and listened too much to Hassayamper. I have always had an idea that Chuck was fearfully like Earp. Isn't he? He rescues and frees the oppressed and the children, looks after a paralysed woman. He punishes criminals, takes those shut-up into the light. The only thing lacking was that he should own building sites. Now he's Earp exactly."

"Beware of telling him that. He may not like Earp."

"But Earp has been gone fifty or sixty years. You are mad about Earp in this town. It's as though all the years since the water flooded the mines were just in parenthesis. That old boy behind me seems your contemporary. So, perhaps, is Earp, for that matter."

"You're so romantic, Swede. Earp died in 1930, and he was here the year before he died. Legally he was still wanted for having shot Billy Clanton and the McLowerys. He had got rich out of oil in California. He came only as far as Boot Hill, and from there he sent for Hassayamper, and they stood and talked for half an hour beside Clanton's grave. Then Earp disappeared, and the following year he died. That was the only time he came back to Tombstone. Thirty minutes. And he was only out at Boot Hill."

"What did they talk about?"

"I don't know. You'd better ask Hassayamper."

We fell silent again.

I had taken the precaution of leaving my wristwatch with Margareta and so had no idea what the time was, nor how the minutes were crawling along. In the end, sitting in there in the dark, I did not know whether I was asleep or awake. Strange thoughts passed through my brain, moving slowly like heavy, stupid animals.

When I came to my senses again, it was only twelve minutes since the soles of Chuck's boots had disappeared into the gallery. I was no longer surprised at anything. We heard a scraping noise, lit our torches and there were the soles again. Inch by inch they backed out over the deep hole.

"It's a slow business," said Chisholm. "He has a kid with him."

I put one foot on a jutting stone and, supporting my left hand against the wall while Chisholm held my wrist, I straddled the hole. I took one of Chuck's feet and guided it to a good stone and then with the same hand tested a clamp and guided his hand to that. I could now hear the commercial traveller's girl. Chuck let his full weight hang on the iron clamp and swiftly swung himself right out.

The girl came crawling.

Chisholm informed us briefly that we had now been down for thirty-four minutes.

After that everything was done efficiently, quickly and with decision. Chuck crawled back into the gallery, after lifting the girl out. She was not frightened by the deep hole or by the darkness, only of the fuss. She bit hard at her lower lip, laid one arm round my neck while I stood there acting as bridge between the gallery and the shelf. Chisholm gently transferred my hand from his to one of the iron clamps and with his freed hand took the girl tightly by the waist and swung her to safety. I then climbed up the steep slope back to the first big shelf, saw the little circle of blue sky and gave a shout.

"We. . . ."

Four heads appeared at the top, and I corrected myself:

"Chuck has found them. They are all right. Sling down the lassoes."

The rope came. I threw one end down to Chisholm with a stone tied to it. I felt almost exhilarated. I even lit a pipe. The girl and the boy came up to where I was. Chisholm followed: Chuck came last. His forehead and nose were scraped raw.

"Damned narrow galleries those," he said.

"How in heaven's name could you climb down?" I asked the children gaily.

"Oh, it was nothing," the boy said sulkily.

It took three quarters of an hour to get us all up.

When we had got the boy to the surface, Titus came jolting in his Chevrolet across the railway track and stones, quite heedless of his springs and body. He jumped out, cheery and humpbacked, and lifted down a large carton.

"Chocolate ice," he called "Chocolate ice for all good children."

He sat down on the step with the children beside him and they began to smear themselves with ice-cream.

Margareta went with the commercial traveller and his children back to his crotcheting wife.

Chuck drove home in his little van.

An hour or so later we were sitting, dirty and scratched, in Crystal Palace when the commercial traveller came up to Titus and me.

"I must give Chuck something. He can have what he likes. All I've got. I must find something."

We pondered this at some length, and in the end I suggested:

"Drive into Tucson and buy a backgammon board, the best they've got. Then buy all the champagne Judah has here and take the backgammon and champagne out to Chuck's. We'll follow you and have a sing-song."

He did that.

Chuck's little wife from Northern Ireland was sweet and gentle, and she taught the commercial traveller to play backgammon. They had a nice home. On the walls there was a picture of Lincoln and another of Churchill, and a rather blurred photograph of a grey house in Belfast with a large family in front of it: the men wore caps and the girls had close-fitting jumpers. Margareta and I took Chisholm and Mary Lou aside and drank to them, at which Chisholm, who had already had one or two, winked at us mightily.

About eleven o'clock that evening I drove across to Hassayamper's and knocked on the door. Without the champagne I would never have dared. After ten minutes or so the Apache queen appeared, but I was no longer intimidated by her haughty expression. I asked if I might talk with Hassayamper. She let me wait a while, then I was invited up to the first floor. I passed the bathrooms Chuck had once spoken of and came into a room that was all walnut and bed. Hassayamper was sitting in a deep armchair by the window.

"Ysabel has told me about the mine today," he said. "I shall send Chuck a thousand dollars."

I did not know how I should put my question. All my boldness had evaporated.

I pulled myself together.

"Down in the mine Chisholm told me that Wyatt Earp came back before he died. There was something he told you out at Boot Hill."

Hassayamper looked at me for a moment, then he began to laugh softly.

"Ugh, that. That wasn't anything."

For a long moment he gazed out through the window.

"After he had killed Clanton and the McLowerys, Earp kept himself indoors. A fortnight later his brother Morgan was killed in Campbell's billiard saloon. It was after that Earp left and never again appeared—except that he killed every cowboy who was in with Clanton and the McLowerys. Just to be sure of having his revenge. Out at Boot Hill that day he learned from the girl selling coca-cola at the gate, who did not know who he was, that I was alive, and he gave her fifty dollars to drive in and get me. We just chatted. He didn't ask me a thing about Tombstone or old friends. It was I who asked him."

"What? Whether he shot Clanton for the sake of the money and the plots?"

Hassayamper gave me a long look.

"Not that," he said finally. "I should have told this before. When Wyatt and Morgan were riding across the prairie together from the Mississippi to the Pacific and sleeping out, they used to wonder what dying was like, the actual last moment. Morgan was the elder by a little, and he insisted that you must see something just as you fell asleep. He thought you would see a promised land, like a valley in California at least. Wyatt did not agree. Now it is an old story, that the night Morgan was murdered in the billiard saloon they laid him on one of the billiard tables—I've got it here in the living room for that matter —and he sent for Wyatt, for there was something he wanted to say to him. Wyatt came and they were alone in there till Morgan died—with half the town in the windows trying to look in over the screens. Morgan lay on the billiard table and Wyatt stood leaning over him holding a miner's lamp in one hand. I remember it myself. Then Wyatt bent down and listened carefully and we outside swore that now Morgan was demanding that he should be avenged. But that day out at Boot Hill in 1929 Wyatt told me that Morgan had merely said that Wyatt had been right and that he, Morgan, didn't see a damned thing.

I was back at the feast in Chuck's honour before midnight. I told Margareta that we might as well stay late, as we must leave Tombstone after the Helldorado and drive west, across the Rockies to the valleys and the sea on the other side.

17

THE HELLDORADO

This morning, I, Billy Clanton, got up at seven o'clock and took a look at my face in the mirror. A streaky beard straggled down towards my pyjama jacket and my moustache drooped as though heavy with egg. I thought I looked dreadful with my yellowish beard and my skin pallid beneath it; my eyes were watery and insane, and altogether I looked like a madman. I woke Margareta and we had coffee and dressed slowly. I was to put on the boots and a heavy cartridge belt, and Margareta was to start the day in her crinoline. She put a shawl protectingly round her shoulders.

We said goodbye on the veranda, for we would not see each other again till the evening in Crystal Palace. Already, at only eight o'clock, we could hear cars hooting on the road, and there was a long string of them halted in front of the schoolhouse, moving forward a few jerky feet at a time towards the parking places up by Toughnut and Lucky Cuss mines.

It was not till I got to the road that it struck me that I was bound to cause a bit of a stir. People began winding down the windows of their cars and calling to me, but I had had clear instructions from the Professor to pay no attention and to play my part from the very start, for otherwise you could not create any illusion. So I sent an imbecile and watery look at those who called out and fingered my revolvers nervously, and that put them in a flurry, for they had reckoned on a playful wave. It gave me a little surge of pleasure to feel that I had frightened them or at least made them uncomfortable.

I did not make for the drugstore and *Epitaph* where the flags were out, but walked on out to OK corral, where I was to meet Slattery, my elder brother. He was there when I arrived; we had a shed in Chisholm's workshop where we assembled. It was part of the Professor's method of production that we should not be told beforehand who was playing whom, and I knew little beyond the fact that Slattery was to be Ike Clanton. The Professor was to be Sheriff Behan, which was bad casting, as Behan had had an innocent childish face. But he had been neutral and run between Clanton and Earp, which made his part the only possible one for the producer of our passion play.

This confirmed my suspicions that Chuck was to be Wyatt Earp. I had long had an inner conviction that he was Wyatt Earp. Next I heard that Chisholm who was then changing trousers inside an old car, was to be Frank McLowery, that Hockstaedt who was sitting asleep in the workshop was to be Tom Mc-Lowery, and that Billy Claibourne, who served in the drugstore, was to play a young, unlicked cowboy. Thus Slattery, Chisholm, Hockstaedt, the boy and I were to be shot down en masse once a day for the next three days.

Beyond that I was told nothing about my part. I was not to know my opponents when I met them revolver in hand.

Then Chisholm emerged from his workshop and handed out little plastic bags filled with tomato sauce.

"You squeeze and burst those inside your shirts when I give the word," he said.

Ours was not an enviable position. In the first place we had to wait a couple of hours while the tourists walked round the town charging themselves with expectation and ate and drank at Crystal Palace, and then we were the ones who lost, we had to be bandits and meet our punishment, be mown down outside in the sun-drenched yard of the corral. The whole point was that we should remain invisible as long as possible.

About two o'clock somebody was to sing out:

"The McLowerys and the Clanton boys are down in the OK corral."

Then Chuck in his black frock-coat would rise from the poker table in Crystal Palace, where he had been sitting all morning with his brothers and Doc Holliday, who obviously would be Titus, and slowly walk towards us; and we would emerge from our hiding place with our beards and wild looks and frighten the life out of the tourists; and then we would be left lying in the dust.

A little Mexican ran across from the nearby milk-bar with a tray of food for us, and we ate bacon and eggs and then lay down and waited, chatting to pass the time. Only idle chat.

The hum of tourists' voices came to us from only a few yards away, but as the morning passed the sound receded further and further, and in the end we were like isolated beasts lying waiting for an opportunity to hurl ourselves upon the innocents outside, hiding in our own wickedness.

All at once Chisholm, who had been in an exceptionally good mood all morning said:

"This is another instance of how silly we are."

"We, who are we?" I asked.

"Not you. But us, the Americans."

There was a moment's silence. Then Slattery gave a low laugh and said:

"Exactly."

I lay quiet and just gazed up at the corrugations of the iron roof; there was nothing I could say, for there was no denying that the whole business was childish.

"It's our mums' fault," said Slattery after a while.

No one said anything to that, and he went on:

"Our daddies have really never been anything but elder brothers. What was Dad to do with one when one was small? He was to give one a baseball bat and teach one to shoot and fish and then the two of you put on overalls and crawled in under the car and fiddled with that. There wasn't much difference in Mum's voice when she spoke to my Dad or to me."

Again there was a momentary silence, then Chisholm changed position with an ill-concealed belch and said:

"What are you getting at?"

"Well," said Slattery, "we do such childish things. We believe in so much that other adult peoples or those with a little experience do not. Of course we get a lot of experience, but it just seems to run off us. When I came back from the war I lived

158

for six months with my parents before I began driving buses. They live in Corpus Christi, Texas. You didn't know there was such a town, did you Swede? Funny name. For a time it was the worst gangsters' hole in Texas. Well, Mum put her hand on my arm and asked to tell them all about the war, and so I let go about Anzio and Monte Cassino and the mud and the hellishness and how the boys tumbled to right and to left of me. But she just went about looking more and more anxious till finally she outed with it: she was wondering about me and girls.

"It's pretty darned queer—there had I lived among bullets and up to my knees in mud, with a brand new chance of dying every minute—but Mum was only worried lest I had got into bed with some tart. I don't know what was troubling her. That I had fallen and got a dose, perhaps. But not really. I think she was afraid lest I had been corrupted, and that I went about desiring some dissolute woman who had turned my head. . . . She still thinks that, that that's why I haven't married. God knows what goes on in Mum's head. Perhaps it's horrid to speak of your mum like this, but I can almost see from her expression that she has some frightful visions of me having been taught to lie in some special way in Europe, she dare not think the thought out, but I can see that she, poor woman, just sees a great lump of flesh stuck together in some revolting way. . . .

"But it's where she got that from that worries me. There's nothing wrong with me is there? It makes me sick that she would think that. That, I mean, is where the curse comes in. We want to be so good. We are so good. I think that's how we're made. I have heard all that about it giving you complexes and that sub-consciously you dream of doing other things. If you're married and shout at the old woman across the kitchen table that's because you really want to lay her naked on the bed and whip her.

"But I can never help feeling that we are born with some sort of inability to do ugly things. It's almost too simple, one's almost ashamed to say it, but I believe that's how it is. We always want to make everything tidy and good and fine. We will go to war for any little ass of a country that gets molested. Friend Swede, I'm not isolationist or anything like that, but I can never understand why we should fight. Hitler takes Europe—so what? We still get our wheaten rolls and our ham and eggs here in Tombstone and where you will in U.S.A. That goes on. The Chinese take Korea—do you think anyone in the U.S.A. is going to be adversely affected by that? There's no mortal reason, no economic or political reason for us to intervene like a bloody fire brigade every time there's a flare-up—not one. That commercial traveller, out-and-out stupid as he is, is right. And Titus too, our old American with roots in Californian soil for almost a generation. Ha, ha, ha.

"What do we want to go and fight for? They say that the U.S.A. can't live if Europe is enslaved. Pah! We live all right now when two-thirds are enslaved. If we had some 'planes flying round day and night, up to the Bering Straits and Hudson Bay and down to the Caribbean, keeping a look-out for Russians and such-like generally, that would be quite enough.

"But, look, it's this way: I still think we ought to fight. We should always be good. Mum tells us that, and so does Miss Beatrice. Miss Beatrice? She was my Sunday School teacher. Fourth Baptist Congregation, Corpus Christi. I imagine she was the loveliest thing I've seen. No, not seen—but experienced. I believed all she said, yet that did not stop me spending hours of an evening lying wondering what she looked like in her under-clothes. I never dared go so far as to imagine her stark. Miss Beatrice inculcated thousands of things into me, and I can still remember her and all she said. It's probable all that is just bad conscience. It's a question of what you call things. I know somehow that we all in some incredible way are driven by a constant urge to do good, whether that is due to Miss Beatrice or Mum or a bad conscience . . . but if Eisenhower or anyone else tell us that we must fight for the rest of the world and for all the small, dirty, free countries, where they have flies on their food and don't clean their nails and the men are like the waiters in Paris and scratch their behinds before they serve you your food, and you get polio and cancer if you drink their milk, and your whole works rot away if you just kiss a girl in the street, and they have the loveliest old cathedrals in the world—well, if Eisenhower tells us that we ought to fight for such little countries, then we do so.

"That's because we know at the bottom of our hearts that we ought to. We are the big brothers. We must help. Help every-body. But Eisenhower can't be like Mum or Miss Beatrice and stand up and say that we ought to do that because we're good

Christians, instead he flatters us by pretending that we're hellish smart fellows who must understand that our export markets will shrink if we don't shoulder arms and march off now, and that, of course, would make our consumer's goods rise in price, and that would cause unemployment, and the air wouldn't be worth breathing, and God knows what else he would think of. And then we nod our pates and nudge each other and say: that's how it is, it's obvious the export markets would shrink, we can't have that, so off we go in tanks and armoured boats, and the quarry-men in every little town on the prairie spit on their hands and begin to prepare a sandstone monument to our glorious dead. Smith, Brown, Adams, Jarecki, Hermanski, Tannenbaum, Nathan Goldstein, Furillo Diaz and Charlie Swanson. They've all been out preventing the export markets from shrinking.

"For right inside us—Adams, whom I've allowed myself to put on the monument, is a negro, if you didn't realize it—inside of us we don't dare admit that it's in order to be good, to do as Mum and Miss Beatrice told us, that we go and fight. Our big noises tell us that it's because we're intelligent and even a bit extra clever, but they do that so that we ourselves shouldn't stop to think how childish we are, how pure-hearted—how we are out fighting in order to do good and be good.

"Oh, we ought to have a large statue in the middle of America, just as big as the Statue of Liberty, and it should be of Miss Beatrice with her sweet little feet and knees—my Beatrice was in 1927 and you saw knees in those days—and she should have one finger raised and underneath should be written: 'Go out, all you who are good and strong from eating big Kansas steaks and rescue those of your playfellows who are trampled upon and persecuted, and dust them off and put their caps back on their heads. . . .'

"And right in the west, a bit out in the Pacific even, we should have another large statue of a hula-hula-donna waggling her hips.

"We are all little obedient, industrious, good children who can't do anything but good, but we are so afraid that might be noticed, that we are almost relieved when Communists and the long-haired gentry tell us that we are capitalistic vultures, for then we can think that at any rate we aren't such babes after all.

"That's why I believe you think us childish, Swede, and you'll go back and have something funny to tell about us so that people get a good cackle at us. Again. Then the Russians'll come and wallop you, and so we'll come rushing, Furillo, Hermanski, Tannenbaum and Chisholm and I, and then we'll pick you up and chase the wicked bully away and dust you off, and then ninety-six professors will be given special grants to work out the value to our export markets of us having gone out in our big salvage van and rescued old Europe; and then we'll straighten our backs, for that makes us realize that we are darned smart and have saved the dollar for a long time ahead, and then an old boy from Kalamazoo in Michigan or Chattanooga in Tennessee will come and buy a picture by Rubens or Goya and take it home, and you will rise up as one man and ask what we kids want with pictures by Rubens and Goya when we have television and Hopalong Cassidy, which you think is pretty well our level."

That ended Slattery's monologue but at first no one in the hot workshop spoke. Then Chisholm changed position on his old car seat and, his forehead wrinkled, asked anxiously,

"Do you mean we oughtn't to have a Helldorado?"

Slattery gave him a long look.

Chisholm at once corrected himself.

"No," he said, "I was just trying to be funny. Too newly married."

From the other side of the garage wall came the hum of the tourists' voices, the sound of the cars edging their way through to the parking places and the tramp of thousands of feet. The last few days I had been suffering from stage fright, but that was all over now.

During Slattery's monologue I had almost forgotten all about the Helldorado. But now our hour was at hand.

I knew how it was to begin: in Crystal Palace the tourists were to see a poker game in full swing as in the old days, with Wyatt Earp and Doc Holliday—imagine, Titus as the Doc!— and professional gamblers in top hats and miners nervously chewing their moustaches. The tourists were even to be allowed to sit down and take a hand, but only with toy money, otherwise it would have been illegal. Then someone would come in and say that the brothers Clanton and McLowery were down in OK corral and that they were kicking up a fuss and were armed and were telling everyone who came along that they were going to wipe out the Earp brothers and all their supporters. Then the Professor was to come as Sheriff Behan and say that he was going down and ask us, McLowerys and Clantons, to ride off quietly or else hand over our guns if we intended to stay, and we were to tell him to go and hide himself.

Then the drama was to come. Wyatt, the Doc and Wyatt's brothers were to make for us, first along Fourth Street, then turning down Fremont and in through the gateway to the corral. We were to give the tourists plenty of time to collect so that they could get a good view, then we would exchange a few nasty remarks, shots would be fired and all would be over. The brothers Earp would walk back in silence after wiping us out.

For three days on end.

"So," said Chisholm, "you think that America is just a Sunday school, that all we do comes from having been taught to do right or at least to try and behave correctly. To be good. We are taught to be good. That is why we go out as sheriffs, pure Wyatt Earps, and make things right when the bad boys have been up to mischief—Hitler and Mussolini and the brothers McLowery and Clanton."

"That's what I think," said Slattery. "I think it's idiotic that it is so, but I do think that's how it really is."

Again I thought of Wyatt Earp: always on the hunt after bad lads, always ready to get the money owing for a piano, quick to draw the revolver at his hip, where it always hung beside the pocket in which he kept his leases and deeds and documents. I thought of Chuck plunging head first into the mine.

"This business of our wanting to get something out of our wars and rescue operations in Korea and Europe, that's merely because we're so embarrassed in case it should appear that we are young kids," said Slattery again. "We are terrified lest we shouldn't look like sufficiently sharp business people. We hide our little Sunday school hearts inside us. That's the whole point of our foreign policy and administration in Washington: the chaps work to make us appear wily and clever, so that no one shall see that we are just good little children. Our best trick is to keep on saying that we are good, hoping that no one will see through us and discover that that is what we really are."

We heard the sound of numbers of running feet behind the shed. A cloud of dust rose from the street outside. We heard voices: women's anxious queries, children's voices full of excitement, fathers trying to sound calm.

The Professor came running through the brilliant sunlight across the corral to play his paltry part as intermediary.

Behind him I saw four black figures, a thin dark line in the flood of sunlight. It was Wyatt Earp and his brothers and Doc Holliday coming to punish me.